# Harvesting Systems and Equipment in British Columbia

**A.J. MacDonald**

Forest Engineering Research Institute
of Canada

FERIC Handbook No. HB-12

*1999*

BRITISH
COLUMBIA Ministry of Forests
Forest Practices Branch

FOREST ENGINEERING
RESEARCH INSTITUTE
OF CANADA

INSTITUT CANADIEN
DE RECHERCHES
EN GÉNIE FORESTIER

**Canadian Cataloguing in Publication Data**
MacDonald, A. J.
Harvesting systems and equipment in British Columbia

(FERIC handbook, ISSN 0701-8355 ; no. HB-12)

Co-published by Forest Engineering Research Institute of Canada.
Includes bibliographical references: p.
Includes index.
ISBN 0-7726-3827-6

1. Logging – British Columbia. 2. Logging – British Columbia –
Machinery. 3. Forest machinery – British Columbia. I. British Colum-
bia. Forest Practices Branch. II. Forest Engineering Research Institute of
Canada. III. Title. IV. Series.

SD388.M32 1999         634.9'8         C99-960106-7


**Prepared by**
Jack MacDonald
Forest Engineering Research Institute of Canada
2601 East Mall
Vancouver, BC  V6T 1Z4
**for**
B.C. Ministry of Forests
Forest Practices Branch
1450 Government St.
Victoria, BC  V8W 3E7
http://www.for.gov.bc.ca/hfp/hfp.htm


**Published by**
B.C. Ministry of Forests
Forestry Division Services Branch
Production Resources
595 Pandora Avenue
Victoria, BC  V8W 3E7


Copies of this report may be obtained, depending on supply, from:
Crown Publications
521 Fort Street
Victoria, BC  V8W 1E7
(250) 386-4636
http://www.crownpub.bc.ca

For more information on Forestry Division publications, visit our web site at
http://www.for.gov.bc.ca/hfd/pubs/index.htm

## Abstract

This handbook describes the various types of equipment and systems used for harvesting timber in British Columbia. Falling, primary transport (ground, cable, and aerial), processing, and loading phases are described in terms of common and distinguishing features and their relationship to operational and environmental considerations. The handbook also discusses the effects of operating techniques, site characteristics, and external requirements from the same operational and environmental perspectives.

Primary operating conditions for the various machine types are outlined in summary tables. A series of flowcharts based on a risk-analysis system is used to rank the probability of conducting successful operations with different equipment on various sites.

## Author

Jack MacDonald is a Senior Researcher in the Harvesting Operations group of FERIC's Western Division. In 1976, he graduated from the University of British Columbia with a Bachelor of Science in Forestry — Harvesting Option, and is a Registered Professional Forester in British Columbia.

After graduation, Jack worked for 10 years as a logging engineer in coastal British Columbia. Since joining FERIC in 1986, Jack has worked on machine and systems evaluations, and has published several reports on ground-based and cable-based harvesting systems. His other work at FERIC has included development of a computer program for GIS-based harvest and silviculture planning.

## Acknowledgements

The author would like to thank all those who contributed to the handbook.

The extensive knowledge of Bela Hirczy was invaluable during the interviews. Bela's understanding of harvesting systems in general and cable logging systems in particular was most appreciated, and his review comments added much to the project.

Each of the woodlands managers, logging superintendents, and operating personnel who contributed during the interviews is acknowledged and thanked. Without their input, this project would not have been possible.

The project was directed by a steering committee comprised of industry and agency personnel who provided guidance during the formative stages of the project, and reviewed the drafts as they were produced. Thank you all for your input. One member of the steering committee in particular provided valuable liaison with the Ministry of Forests: the contribution of Larry Sluggett to the project is expressly acknowledged.

Tony Sauder and Ingrid Hedin reviewed early versions of the handbook, and provided valuable guidance for its conclusion. Shelley Corradini created the artwork, for which the author is grateful. FERIC researchers who participated in the review workshop are acknowledged and thanked for their contributions.

## Disclaimer

# CONTENTS SUMMARY

# CONTENTS

**Tables**

# Harvesting Systems and Equipment
# Part One
## EQUIPMENT SELECTION

*The handbook does not attempt to define a single "best" system for any site. Instead, it presumes that readers need to be aware of the key factors that influence the probability of achieving success with any given combination of equipment and site characteristics. Readers will then use their own judgement to evaluate the merits of the various options. The information in the handbook should be considered only as part of an overall process for equipment selection which will vary from company to company.*

# INTRODUCTION

Many different harvesting systems and equipment are available for today's logger. Options range from small skidders to large skylines to helicopters, with a wide variety in between. Two of the most important tasks faced by the logger are to select the best harvesting system and equipment for a given site, and to use the selected equipment in the best way possible. Each system can operate successfully under a wide range of conditions, and the conditions suitable to each system can overlap considerably. On many sites, several systems could be used successfully, yet the conditions on other sites may favour a single harvesting system.

Sometimes the choice between harvesting systems and equipment may result from personal or corporate preferences, especially if the options are similar. In other cases, the same equipment can be used on different sites, but the operating techniques must be changed to achieve the desired results. Regardless of the selection process, understanding both the economic and environmental ramifications of choosing a particular type of equipment for use on any given site is necessary.

In addition to economic, corporate, and environmental considerations, harvest-system selections can have legal implications. Depending on the jurisdiction, planners may choose equipment that meets criteria or achieves results in certain site conditions as required by various regulations.

With so many factors to consider, how does a person decide which harvesting equipment and system is best suited for a particular site? While there are as many different ways to arrive at a decision as there are loggers, planners, and equipment owners, each decision should be based on a thorough understanding of the implications of selecting the different equipment types. Better understanding will lead to better decisions, and the objective of this handbook is to help improve that understanding.

The handbook describes the various harvesting systems and equipment commonly used in British Columbia. It describes various site characteristics, operating techniques, and external requirements, and their effect on different types of harvesting equipment. The information contained herein can help the logger or planner make better choices. However, the handbook is not meant to be used as a rigid guide — its role is mainly for reference.

## About This Handbook

### Background

The British Columbia Ministry of Forests approached FERIC in 1995 to prepare an educational resource about harvesting systems and equipment. The new *Forest Practices Code of British Columbia Act* required licensees to identify harvesting systems in logging plans, and ministry personnel to review the intended use of those systems and equipment. However, information was lacking — no common descriptions existed of what equipment was available for timber harvesting in British Columbia, and what the capabilities were of that equipment. This handbook resulted from those discussions.

While this handbook grew out of a requirement of the *Forest Practices Code of British Columbia Act*, FERIC's advisory committee was apprehensive about its possible role regarding harvest planning and the Forest Practices Code. The committee wanted to ensure that the handbook could not be misinterpreted as providing a "cookbook" formula to determine the "correct" equipment to use for any particular harvesting site. In addition, it was recognized that this handbook would likely serve a wider audience than British Columbia; such an audience may not be interested in the legal requirements for timber harvesting in British Columbia. Lastly, it was recognized that legislation is subject to change, and that linking the handbook closely with the requirements of the Forest Practices Code might limit its usefulness if the requirements of the Forest Practices Code were to change.

As a result of these concerns, the handbook provides information about the capabilities of the various systems and equipment, but does not link them directly to the requirements of the Forest Practices Code. That task is left to the reader as a separate exercise.

### Organization

The handbook is divided into two parts.

Part 1 reviews the context of equipment selection, summarizes the primary characteristics of various types of equipment, and lists the key factors to consider when matching harvesting equipment to sites. It also includes several examples of using the handbook to select candidate harvesting systems for specific site conditions.

Part 2 provides more detailed reference information about the various types of equipment and working conditions. It describes the harvesting phases, operating techniques, site characteristics, and external requirements, and their effect on the suitability of the different equipment types to various sites. The phases are primary transport, falling, processing, and loading. Primary transport is presented first, even though it occurs after falling, because it is commonly used to describe and classify harvesting systems.

The information in Part 1 is presented as a series of tables outlining the equipment characteristics, and charts outlining the key factors to consider for equipment selection. The reference sections in Part 2 are organized around common characteristics and distinguishing characteristics for the various equipment types. The common characteristics are those that define a particular type of equipment — they make a machine what it is. On the other hand, the distinguishing characteristics separate the various makes and models of equipment from similar machines within the same type.

These characteristics, the basis of the equipment-selection process, are also the factors that make one machine suitable for use on a particular site while rendering another machine unsuitable.

The descriptions in Part 2 explain the effects of each factor from operational and environmental perspectives. The operational perspectives include machine productivity, log quality, safety, and others, while the environmental items include soil disturbance, water quality, and long-term forest productivity.

### Intended audience

This handbook is intended for two different audiences. The first group consists of people interested in timber-harvesting processes, but who may have only a rudimentary understanding of harvesting systems and equipment. Resource agency officers or other government officials who deal with timber harvesting only incidentally may find pertinent information in the handbook that can help with their job functions. Inexperienced foresters can also use the handbook to broaden their exposure to harvesting systems and equipment. The second group is people such as equipment operators and planners who are more experienced in timber harvesting in their own locale, but who want to learn about systems used in other regions of the province. The handbook may provide them with new information that can be taken from one region and applied to their local operations.

The handbook can be used in various ways depending on the reader's objectives. The reader can follow the charts from Part 1 to rank the relative risk of using different machine types under various conditions, and then seek specific information about the equipment in Part 2. Alternatively, reading through each section in Part 2 will provide the reader with a more complete overview of the capabilities and limitations of the various equipment types.

The handbook is intended to provide a broad overview of the capabilities and limitations of the various equipment types. After browsing the handbook, the reader will have a basic introduction to the capabilities of the harvesting equipment commonly used in British Columbia.

## Background to Equipment Selection

### Context for equipment selection

This section provides a very brief overview of the issues involved with equipment selection. It is intended for readers who may be inexperienced with equipment selection, but who are required to specify equipment to use for a particular cutblock. It will focus the reader's attention on those factors that are most important for that cutblock.

However, this handbook does not intend to suggest that any particular make, model, or type of equipment must be used on a specific site. That decision must rest with the various planners and owners responsible for managing the area.

*Why is equipment selection important?*

Each cutblock has a set of management objectives that likely include aspects of safety, profitability, forest health, water quality, and environmental concerns. If the equipment and system chosen for a cutblock are mismatched to the site and stand conditions, then it may be impossible to achieve any or all of these objectives. The ramifications of improper equipment selection may range from unsafe working conditions to unacceptable costs to charges under the applicable forest-practices legislation. Making sound choices aims to reduce the risk of those events happening.

*Who selects the equipment and when?*

Many people make decisions about equipment selection at different times. These include:

- Equipment owner or corporate financial officer — matches the equipment fleet to the long-term expected site conditions to ensure that the equipment is profitable to operate over the long term. Decisions made when buying the equipment.

- Layout personnel — ensures that the road and cutblock boundary locations are suitable to the type of equipment that will be used for harvesting. Decisions made at layout time.

- Planner and woodlands manager — ensures a balance between equipment availability and number of cutblocks laid out for particular equipment types. Decisions made periodically (e.g., monthly or annually).

- Woodlands supervisor or contractor — assigns specific machines to work on specific sites. Fine-tunes the layout and operating techniques to match the site characteristics. Decisions made at harvest time.

*What factors affect equipment selection?*

**Terrain**   The factors to consider include slope, ground profile, streams and wetlands, gullies, and roughness. These factors affect the ability of the equipment to travel over the ground to reach the operating sites. Driving access is required to all parts of the cutblock for ground-based equipment, while cable and aerial systems allow for remote access. Ground-based systems may cause more soil disturbance than cable or aerial systems, especially on steep slopes or rough ground. The ground profile is critical to the success of cable systems — the layout must be engineered with adequate deflection and ground clearance to support the intended payload. In general, ground-based systems are less expensive to own and operate than cable systems, which are less expensive than aerial. Sensitive areas must be considered carefully to ensure that soil disturbance or other environmental damage does not occur.

**Soil**   Soil characteristics to consider during equipment selection include texture, moisture content, and seasonal impact. These factors affect the bearing strength of the soil, and its ability to withstand machine traffic without degradation. Fine-textured soils and moist soils are more sensitive to machine traffic than coarse-textured or dry soils. Frozen or deep-snow conditions allow ground-based machines to access ground that may not support traffic during non-frozen conditions.

**Timber characteristics**   The following timber characteristics can influence equipment selection: tree size, volume per hectare, and timber quality. There are two primary concerns: (1) the physical ability of the equipment to handle the trees without causing unsafe working conditions or causing damage to the equipment, site, or timber; and (2) harvesting economics for both per-tree and per-cutblock costs. Small trees are less economical to harvest than large trees, and small cutblocks are less economical than large cutblocks. Fixed costs such as road construction must be amortized over the volume harvested from the cutblock, and lower volumes per hectare result in smaller cutblock volumes and higher costs. Harvesting systems with high mobilization costs, such as cable or aerial systems, are especially susceptible to the effects of low volumes per hectare. The timber quality affects the timber value, and thus the harvesting economics. Large trees may be too heavy for some equipment to handle, and small trees may be damaged by large equipment.

**Business requirements**   The timber must be harvested safely and economically for the licensee and its contractors to ensure worker safety and to remain in business. All costs, including ownership, operating, and maintenance costs, must be considered

Business requirements, as opposed to site characteristics, may impose conditions on the harvesting operations. These business requirements may include the operating season, timber flow, mill's log specifications, amount of work available, unique operating methods, labour availability, and equipment availability, service, and transportation.

Each company chooses harvesting equipment and methods that it feels best meets its corporate objectives, and different corporate objectives can be reflected in the equipment selection. For example, the mill may be equipped to accept a certain wood form as input (e.g., whole stems, logs, short logs); therefore, the harvesting system must be geared to produce that wood form. This choice can have ramifications throughout all phases of harvesting.

*Weather and climate*  Inclement weather such as rain or wind can affect the severity of soil disturbance or can cause more hazardous working conditions. Saturated soils are more susceptible than dry soils to damage from machine traffic. Wind is especially problematic for hand-fallers. Deep snow can provide a protective ground covering for machines to travel upon, although it can also impair machines' mobility. Snow on steep terrain creates a safety hazard for on-the-ground workers because of slippery footing.

*Silvicultural system*  The silvicultural system is significant for equipment selection because some machines can maneuver better than others between the standing trees and extract logs from a partial cut without damaging the residual stand or affecting future growth potential. Machine size and maneuverability are important issues to consider in relation to silvicultural systems.

*Legislation, regulations, or permit requirements*  Some of the operating parameters in the cutblocks result from legislative requirements or permit conditions required by government. For example, utilization standards may include acceptable limits for stump heights and levels of breakage. Soil disturbance guidelines can limit the number of roads, trails, and other access structures that are allowed to be constructed on various sites, and thus affect the range of candidate equipment.

## Planning horizon for equipment selection

Selecting the equipment for a particular site must be made within the current corporate and regulatory environment. Some typical questions to ask might be: What equipment is available? What is the long- and short-term budgeted production? What are the log quality requirements for the mill? What capital is available? What special environmental factors must be considered? Sometimes, different equipment can be selected upon short notice, but more often the equipment available for any specific site is limited by budgets or by other long-term commitments. Therefore, harvesting equipment selection must be considered over both the long term and the short term.

Over the long term, the general site and timber characteristics that are expected must be examined, and the equipment fleet selected to suit those conditions. The time horizon, which is related to budget and capital amortization, is generally three to five years or longer for major capital purchases.

Contractual and corporate obligations mean there is less flexibility to choose different equipment in the short term, and the equipment selection question is reversed. The site and stand characteristics remain important, but instead of asking "What equipment is suited to this site?" the question becomes "What site is available to use this equipment?" The process of matching equipment to sites becomes a matter of ensuring an adequate number of suitable sites for the available equipment.

These long- and short-term considerations apply not only to large companies, but also to independent contractors and planners with the Ministry of Forests Small Business Forest Enterprise Program. The difference between them is a matter of degree, especially regarding the control over each planning level. Large companies that incorporate both planning and operational functions control their long- and short-term planning — to a large extent, they control their own destiny within their corporate structure. On the other hand, long- and short-term plans are provided to contractors — their equipment selection decisions are based on the information contained in the plans provided to them.

Planners for the Ministry of Forests Small Business Forest Enterprise Program do not purchase equipment themselves, but they do influence the choices made by logging contractors by way of their future timber sale opportunities and the conditions placed on specific timber sales.

### What constitutes successful harvesting operations?

The success of a particular harvesting system can be measured against operational and environmental criteria. The operational criteria include such factors as safety, profitability, and log quality, while the environmental criteria include water quality, soil disturbance, and residual stand protection. These objectives will change in importance depending on the site and the outlook of the observer. For example, the contractor may rank profitability before residual stand protection, while the forester may reverse their importance. However, both operational and environmental criteria must be considered to harvest timber successfully in today's corporate and environmental climate.

## EQUIPMENT DESCRIPTIONS

The various types of harvesting equipment are described in two sets of graphics. The first set summarizes the costs and characteristics of various equipment types in a tabular format using a High-Medium-Low rating system. By scanning the "characteristics" tables, the reader can quickly determine whether a particular type of equipment is suitable to various site conditions and operating environments.

The second set identifies the key factors that affect the likelihood of conducting successful operations with various equipment types. By following through these charts, the reader can quickly identify those site characteristics that imply high risk with any given type of equipment.

Neither set of graphics attempts to identify the "correct" equipment for a particular site because there are usually too many variables for there to be just one feasible solution. Instead, these graphics can help to focus the reader's attention on those equipment types that have the lowest risk and the highest probability of achieving success.

After reading this section, the reader may wish to consult Part 2 of the handbook for more detailed information about specific equipment types.

### What Equipment To Consider?

The tables and charts presented later in this section have been developed assuming that all equipment types are available to be used on any given site, and that a selection process will eliminate the less suitable types. Given the full range of equipment to choose from, cost is often the first selection criteria. However, cost is not the only consideration, and depending on the circumstances, may not even be the primary consideration. For example, a cutblock with sensitive soils may require specialized equipment for harvesting to proceed at all, and costs become a secondary consideration.

The planner must carefully consider all available options for harvesting systems, and a starting point is to consider the range of equipment costs. Relative cost ranges of various equipment types are shown in Table 1.

Costs can be considered in various ways, including unit production costs, ownership costs, and total costs. Unit production costs include the machine's operating and maintenance costs coupled with an estimate of productivity. Ownership costs include the machine's purchase price, plus interest on capital and other fixed costs such as insurance. Total costs represent the total cost of owning, operating, and repairing the equipment over its lifespan. Low initial costs may not necessarily result in the lowest total costs over the equipment because of high maintenance costs or low productivity.

Costs can also vary widely depending on operating conditions and techniques. For example, Table 1 lists loader-forwarders in the low-cost category for unit production costs, which is accurate for easy terrain with large timber, but is inaccurate for rough terrain or small timber. The unit production costs for Table 1 are applicable under ideal conditions.

Total costs are important to consider, but also difficult to quantify because of different operating conditions and techniques, and widely varying maintenance regimes. Total costs are omitted from Table 1 because of their even wider variability than unit production costs and capital costs.

Unit production costs and ownership costs should be considered separately because they are not always related. For example, helicopters have both high unit production costs and high ownership costs, while clambunk skidders have high ownership costs but low unit production costs. Furthermore, different companies place different emphasis on unit production and ownership costs.

In the long term, all options from Table 1 should be considered, but in the short term only those machine types that are available need be considered.

**Table 1.** *Relative cost ranges for primary transport equipment under ideal conditions*

| Cost range | Unit production costs | Ownership costs |
|---|---|---|
| Low cost | Wheeled skidder<br>Loader-forwarder<br>Cherry picker/Super snorkel<br>Grapple yarder | Wheeled skidder<br>Horse<br>Small-scale equipment |
| Medium cost | Crawler skidder<br>Clambunk skidder<br>Forwarder<br>Horse<br>Small-scale equipment<br>Highlead<br>Small single-span skyline | Crawler skidder<br>Flex-track skidder<br>Highlead<br>Small single-span skyline<br>Multi-span skyline |
| High cost | Flex-track skidder<br>Large single-span skyline<br>Multi-span skyline<br>Medium-lift helicopter | Clambunk skidder<br>Forwarder<br>Cherry picker/Super snorkel<br>Loader-forwarder<br>Grapple yarder<br>Large single-span skyline<br>Medium-lift helicopter |
| Very high cost | Heavy-lift helicopter | Heavy-lift helicopter |

## Equipment Characteristics Summarized by Phase

After using ownership costs or unit production costs to rank the various types of available equipment, the next step is to use equipment characteristics to match equipment to operating conditions. To help with this process, this section presents tables for each harvesting phase that summarize the major features of different equipment types. Four tables are presented: primary transport in Table 2, falling in Table 3, processing in Table 4, and loading in Table 5.

The rows in each table list the important characteristics that can be used to match equipment to operating conditions. The various types of equipment that can be used for each phase are listed in columns across the tables, and the entries in the tables contain a variety of information. In some cases, a High-Medium-Low system is used to rank the various equipment according to each characteristic. In other cases, the tables list actual values such as maximum yarding or skidding distances or maximum slope limits for ground-based equipment. Lastly, "+" or "-" symbols are used to indicate whether a particular feature will enhance or detract from the various characteristics.

In keeping with the objectives of this handbook, the terms "high, medium, and low" are left undefined in the tables. Defining these terms would tend towards a "cookbook" approach for determining the single "correct" answer, which the handbook tries to avoid. Instead, the tables should be used only to rank equipment types *relative to one another*. For example, the required operator skill level for skidders is listed as low, implying only that less skill is required to operate skidders than clambunks, forwarders, or other machines. This list does not say that skidder operators are unskilled. On the contrary, skidder operators require a significant amount of skill and training, especially considering the consequences if the machines are operated in an unsafe or environmentally risky fashion. However, the mechanical simplicity of skidders as compared with forwarders and the reduced manual dexterity as compared with yarding cranes places skidders in the "low" operator skill category.

Using the list of equipment ranked by cost, the reader should determine whether each type of equipment remains a candidate for consideration. As stated previously, costs may not be the primary consideration, and the list of candidate equipment could be ranked by different criteria. Items such as skidding distance, tree size, slope, and susceptibility to high soil moisture will help to eliminate types that are unsuitable for the anticipated site conditions. Other items such as safety hazards, daily productivity, ability to work independently, and capital investment will help to determine whether the equipment will fit within the corporate organizational structure.

After completing the rankings from these tables, the reader should move on to the next section — determining various risk levels.

## Risk-level Assessment

### Risk levels
Acceptable results by a specific equipment type cannot be guaranteed on a given site because too many variables are involved — prescription, operator skill and attitude, weather, business objectives, and quality of site description. Instead, an element of uncertainty or risk is implied, especially when operating techniques are considered. For example, wheeled skidders can be operated safely on gentle slopes, but become unstable on steep slopes especially if turning is required. To increase the safety factor, skidders can be operated straight down the slope or from excavated trails. However,

**Table 2.** *Characteristics of primary transport equipment*

Column groups — Ground: Wheeled skidder - line, Wheeled skidder - grapple, Crawler skidder - line, Crawler skidder - grapple, Flex-track skidder - line, Flex-track skidder - grapple, Clambunk, Forwarder, Loader-forwarder, Cherry picker/Super snorkel, Horse, Small scale. Cable: Highlead, Swing yarder - grapple, Swing yarder - dropline, Small single-span skyline, Large single-span skyline, Multi-span skyline. Aerial: Heavy-lift helicopter, Medium-lift helicopter.

| Characteristics of primary transport equipment | W.skidder-line | W.skidder-grapple | Cr.skidder-line | Cr.skidder-grapple | Flex-track-line | Flex-track-grapple | Clambunk | Forwarder | Loader-forwarder | Cherry picker/Super snorkel | Horse | Small scale | Highlead | Swing yarder-grapple | Swing yarder-dropline | Small single-span skyline | Large single-span skyline | Multi-span skyline | Heavy-lift helicopter | Medium-lift helicopter |
|---|---|---|---|---|---|---|---|---|---|---|---|---|---|---|---|---|---|---|---|---|
| **PERSONNEL** | | | | | | | | | | | | | | | | | | | | |
| Safety hazards | H | M | H | M | H | M | L | L | L | L | H | H | H | M | H | M | H | H | H | H |
| Crew size | M | L | M | L | M | L | L | L | L | L | L | L | M-H | L | M | M | H | M | H | M |
| Operator skill level required | L | L | L | L | M | M | M | M | M | H | M | L | M | H | H | M | H | H | VH | VH |
| Level of supervision required | M | M | M | M | M | M | L-M | M | M-H | L | M | L | M | M | M | M | H | H | VH | VH |
| **LAYOUT** | | | | | | | | | | | | | | | | | | | | |
| Layout skill level | L | L | L | L | M | M | M | M | M | L | L | L | M | M | M | M | H | H | M | M |
| Typical distance to cutblock boundary (m) | 200 | 200 | 200 | 150 | 200 | 200 | 300 | 300 | 120 | 50 | 80 | 150 | 200 | 150 | 300 | 200 | 400 | 500 | 1500 | 1500 |
| Long-distance operating range (m) | 300 | 250 | 250 | 200 | 300 | 250 | 800 | 800 | 200 | 50 | 100 | 200 | 300 | 200 | 400 | 250 | 700 | 800 | 2000 | 2000 |
| Road density | M | M | M | M | M | M | L | L | H | n/a | H | H | H | H | M | M | L | L | L | L |
| Requires landings | Y | N | Y | N | Y | N | N | N | N | n/a | N | N | Y | N | Y | Y | Y | Y | Y * | Y * |
| Suitability to partial cut | M | L | M | L | M | L | L | H | M | L | H | H | L | L | H | H | L | H | M | M |
| **SITE** | | | | | | | | | | | | | | | | | | | | |
| Low-risk favourable slope limits (%) | 35 | 35 | 35 | 35 | 35 | 35 | 35 | 35 | 35 | n/a | 25 | n/a | n/a | n/a | n/a | n/a | n/a | n/a | n/a | n/a |
| High-risk favourable slope limits (%) | 40 | 40 | 50 | 50 | 60 | 60 | 55 | 35 | 35 | n/a | 25 | n/a | n/a | n/a | n/a | n/a | n/a | n/a | n/a | n/a |
| Adverse slope limits (%) | 10 | 10 | 15 | 15 | 20 | 20 | 10 | 15 | 20 | n/a | 5 | 5 | n/a | n/a | n/a | n/a | n/a | n/a | n/a | n/a |
| Preferred direction | downhill | downhill | downhill | downhill | downhill | downhill | downhill | downhill | downhill | up | downhill | | up | dn | uphill | uphill | uphill | uphill | downhill | downhill |
| Soil strength required | H | H | H | H | M | M | M | M | M | n/a | H | L-M | L | L | L | L | L | L | n/a | n/a |
| Ability to avoid causing soil disturbance | L-M | L-M | L-M | L-M | L-M | L-M | M | M | M-H | n/a | H | H | M | M | M | M | H | H | H | H |
| Suitability for small trees | H | H | H | H | H | H | H | H | M | M | H | H | M | L | M | M | L | M | L | M |
| Suitability for large trees | H | H | H | H | H | H | H | H | H | L | L | L | H | H | H | H | H | H | load limit | load limit |
| Adaptability to low volumes/ha | H | H | H | H | H | H | M | H | M | M | H | H | M | L-M | M | M | L | M | L | M |
| **WEATHER RESTRICTIONS** | | | | | | | | | | | | | | | | | | | | |
| Susceptibility to high soil moisture | H | H | H | H | H | H | M-H | M | M-H | n/a | H | M | L-M | L | L | L | L | L | L | L |
| Susceptibility to poor visibility (fog) | L | L | L | L | L | L | L | L | L | L | L | L | M | H | M | M | H | M | H | H |
| Susceptibility to high winds | L | L | L | L | L | L | L | L | L | L | L | L | M | M | M | M | M | M | H | H |
| Restricted by deep snow | M | M | L | L | L | L | L | L | M | L | H | M | H | M | H | H | H | H | H | H |
| Ability to work at night | L | H | L | H | L | H | H | H | M | M | L | L | L | M | L | L | L | L | n/a | n/a |
| **CORPORATE** | | | | | | | | | | | | | | | | | | | | |
| Ability to work independently of loader | L | H | L | H | L | H | H | H | H | H | H | H | L | H | H | M | L | L | L | L |
| Capital investment | L | M | M | M-H | M | M-H | H | H | H | H | L | L | M | H | H | M | H | M | VH | H |
| Hourly productivity | M | M-H | L | M | M | M | H | M | H | H | L | L | M | H | H | M | M | L | VH | H |
| Unit production cost range | L-M | L-M | M | M | M-H | M-H | L | M | L | L | M-H | M | M | L | M | M | H | H | VH | H |

* Helicopters can transport logs either to landings or to water drop-zones.

**Table 3.** *Characteristics of falling equipment*

| Characteristics of falling equipment | Rating* — Type | | | | | Rating* — Carrier | | | Modifications** — Head | | | Modifications** — Features | | | | | | |
|---|---|---|---|---|---|---|---|---|---|---|---|---|---|---|---|---|---|---|
| | Hand-falling | Feller-buncher | Feller-director | Single-grip feller-processor | Double-grip feller-processor | Tracked, boom-type | Wheeled, boom-type | Wheeled, drive-to-tree | High-speed disc | Low-speed disc | Director/chainsaw | Leveling cab | Zero-clearance tailswing | Accumulator | Large-range side-tilt | Rigid head-to-boom attachment | High stability at long reach | Overhead visibility |
| **PERSONNEL** | | | | | | | | | | | | | | | | | | |
| Safety hazards | H | L | L | L | L | L-M | L | M | + | | | + | | | + | | - | - |
| Operator skill level required | H | M | M | H | H | M | M | L-M | + | | | - | | + | | - | | |
| **SYSTEM** | | | | | | | | | | | | | | | | | | |
| Ability to avoid causing soil disturbance | H | M | M | H | H | type limit | | L-M | | | | - | | | + | | + | |
| Suitability for partial cutting in open stand | H | H | M | H | H | M | H | L | | | + | + | + | | + | + | + | + |
| Suitability for partial cutting in dense stand | L | H | L | M | M | M | M | L | | | + | + | ++ | + | + | ++ | ++ | ++ |
| Suitability for choker extraction | H | H | H | L | L | type limit*** | | | | | | | | + | | | | |
| Suitability for grapple skidder extraction | L | H | M | L | L | type limit | | | | | | | | + | + | + | + | |
| Suitability for grapple yarder extraction | H | H | M | L | L | type limit | | | | | | | | + | + | + | + | |
| Suitability for forwarder extraction | L | L | L | H | H | type limit | | | | | | | | | | | | |
| Ability to sort | L | M | L | H | M-H | type limit | | M | | | | | | + | + | + | + | |
| **SITE** | | | | | | | | | | | | | | | | | | |
| Maximum slope (%) | n/a | carrier limit | | | | 60 | 30 | 20 | | | | ++ | | | + | | + | |
| Immunity to obstacles | H | M | M | M | M | H | M | L | - | | | | | | | | + | |
| Ability to work in dense underbrush | L | H | M | L | L | H | H | L | + | | -- | | | | | | | |
| Suitability for small trees | M | H | M | H | L | M-H | M-H | H | + | - | + | | | | ++ | | | |
| Suitability for large trees | H | M | H | L | H | M | L-M | M-H | - | + | - | + | | | | + | + | |
| Suitability for windfall | L-M | M | M | H | H | M | L-M | L | - | + | + | + | | | | ++ | | |
| **WEATHER RESTRICTIONS** | | | | | | | | | | | | | | | | | | |
| Ability to work during high winds | L | M | L | M | M | M | M | M | | | - | | | | | | | |
| Ability to work under deep snow conditions | L | H | H | L | M | H | M | L | + | + | - | | | | | | | |
| Ability to work at night | L | H | H | H | H | | | | | | | | | | | | | |
| **CORPORATE** | | | | | | | | | | | | | | | | | | |
| Capital investment | L | H | M | H | H | H | H | M | | | - | + | + | + | + | | + | + |
| Daily productivity | L | H | M | M | H | H | M | M | + | | | + | | + | | | + | + |
| Unit production costs | variable | | | | | H | H | L | | | | - | | - | | | - | - |

\* Rating: Low to High for this characteristic.
\*\* Modification: + indicates that adding this feature will increase the characteristic, - indicates decrease, blank is neutral.
\*\*\* Type limit: governed by the type, rather than by the carrier.

Table 4. *Characteristics of processing equipment*

| Characteristics of processing equipment | Delimbers/Processors | | | | | | Other | | | |
|---|---|---|---|---|---|---|---|---|---|---|
| | Hand-bucking | Small dangle-head processor | Large dangle-head processor | Small-stroke delimber | Large-stroke delimber | Pull-through delimber | Chain-flail delimber/debarker | Chipper | Hogger | Slasher |
| **SYSTEM** | | | | | | | | | | |
| Safety hazards | H | L | L | L | L | L | H | M | M | L |
| Suitability to landings | H | H | H | H | H | H | H | H | H | H |
| Suitability to roadside | L-M | M | H | H | H | L | L | L-M | L | M-H |
| **SITE** | | | | | | | | | | |
| Suitability for small trees | L-M | H | M | H | M | H | H | H | n/a | H |
| Suitability for large trees | H | L | H | M | H | H | M | L | n/a | L |
| Maximum tree diameter (cm) | n/a | 50 | 80 | 50 | 70 | n/a | n/a | 40 | | n/a |
| **CAPABILITY** | | | | | | | | | | |
| Delimbing | + | + | + | + | + | + | + | - | - | - |
| Topping | + | + | + | + | + | - | - | - | - | + |
| Log measuring | + | + | + | + | + | - | - | - | - | + |
| Butt-rot removal | + | + | + | + | + | - | - | - | - | + |
| Midstem-rot removal | + | + | + | + | + | - | - | - | - | - |
| Can work without support equipment | - | + | + | + | + | - | - | - | - | + |
| Extraction from log deck | n/a | L | M-H | M | H | n/a | n/a | n/a | n/a | M |
| Sorting | n/a | M | M | M | H | n/a | n/a | n/a | n/a | M |
| **CORPORATE** | | | | | | | | | | |
| Capital investment | L | H | H | H | H | L | M | H | H | M |
| Daily productivity | M | H | H | H | H | M | H | H | H | H |

**Table 5.** *Characteristics of loading equipment*

| Characteristics of loading equipment | Type | | | | | Carrier | |
|---|---|---|---|---|---|---|---|
| | Front-end loader | Hydraulic | Butt 'n top | Line loader | Self-loading log truck | Wheeled carrier | Tracked carrier |
| **PERSONNEL** | | | | | | | |
| Safety hazards | L | L | L | M | M | | |
| Operator skill level required | L | L | M | H | L | | |
| **CAPABILITY** | | | | | | | |
| Suitability for small logs | H | M | H | M | H | | |
| Suitablility for large logs | H | H | L-M | H | L-M | | |
| Ability to reach below grade | L | M-H | M | H | M | | |
| Maximum reaching distance (m) | 5 | 15 | 15 | 30+ | 10 | | |
| Able to load from side of truck | H | M | H | M | H | | |
| Able to load from front of truck | n/a | H | L | H | n/a | | |
| Able to load from rear of truck | n/a | H | L | H | n/a | | |
| Cherry-picking, primary transport | L | H | L | H | L | - | |
| **LAYOUT** | | | | | | | |
| Space requirements while loading | H | L | M | M | L | + | - |
| Suitability for landings | H | H | L | H | H | | |
| Suitability for roadside | L | H | H | H | H | - | + |
| Suitability to load from several sites concurrently | H | M | L | L-M | H | + | - |
| Required level of travel surface preparation | M | L | L | H | n/a | + | |
| **CORPORATE** | | | | | | | |
| Capital investment | L | M-H | H | H | L | | + |

excavated trails may have an impact on soil erosion, water quality, or the amount of site disturbance. Similarly, flotation mats can allow excavators to work on soft ground, but may slow machine travel and reduce productivity.

Most importantly, each machine type is suitable to a range of conditions as defined by its basic features. When operating the machine within its appropriate range, the risk of exceeding operational and environmental limits is minimized, but operating outside the range will increase the risk of generating unacceptable results. Even the most benign harvesting system can produce unacceptable results if used inappropriately, and seemingly unsuitable equipment can be made suitable by incorporating appropriate techniques.

Under this concept, selecting the appropriate equipment for each site becomes a matter of matching features to risk. The planner must understand the basic features of the equipment, the range of operating techniques, the influence of site conditions and the external requirements that might be imposed, and how these four factors are related to one another by risk levels. Combinations of equipment and conditions with low risk levels should be considered rather than those with higher risk levels. The use of higher risk combinations may be appropriate under certain operating conditions or to achieve specific goals, but such a selection should be made only with a full understanding of all the potential risks and benefits.

This handbook uses a system of risk evaluation, and Table 6 defines various risk levels on a scale from 1 to 6. These risk levels are not absolute; instead they indicate the relative amount of risk of operating the machine under varying site and objective conditions. A low risk level indicates a good chance of successful operations, while a high number indicates a high risk of failure.

Some high risk activities are constrained by environmental considerations (e.g., high likelihood of soil degradation by wheeled skidders on moist, fine-textured soils), while others are constrained by operational considerations such as productivity (e.g., poor performance of large highlead systems with small trees). In either case, the risk level is shown as a single value, and the underlying cause is not indicated in the charts. The descriptions in Part 2 of the handbook will provide additional detail and explanation regarding the cause of the high risk level.

The high-risk levels as defined in Table 6 and used in the charts that follow are quite definite, whereas the lower levels should be considered more as general guidelines. For

**Table 6.** *Risk-level descriptions*

| Risk Level | Description |
| --- | --- |
| 1 | Minimal risk, best operating conditions. |
| 2 | Generally acceptable; normal operating conditions. Unusual circumstances may increase risk. |
| 3 | Acceptable under many conditions, but exercise caution. |
| 4 | Risky; good reasons or special operating techniques required to operate under these conditions. |
| 5 | Highly risky; exceptional circumstances required to operate under these conditions. Special planning and operating techniques will be required. |
| 6 | Not recommended. |

example, Chart 13 for multi-span skylines lists only four possible outcomes, three of which are risk level 5 or 6, and one of which is risk level 1. This should be interpreted as saying "Three factors rule out multi-span systems. In the absence of these factors, the system is feasible." In contrast, Chart 15 for large skylines lists more factors, some of which have mid-level risks. These mid-level risks indicate that the equipment and site are compatible, but caution should be exercised.

Risk factors that apply to all harvesting systems are shown in Table 7. These factors should be considered, and used to modify the risk factors shown in the individual charts.

**Key factors**

The following charts list the key factors to consider when determining the suitability of each machine type for operating on a particular site. Only the most important factors have been listed — clearly, other factors must be considered when choosing equipment, and the reader should refer to Part 2 of the handbook for additional information. This is especially critical for the low- and mid-level risks — whereas the high-level risks are more definite.

The charts are presented as flowcharts starting from the upper-left corner of each chart. The various factors are shown in diamond-shaped boxes, and the risk levels are shown in small rectangular boxes. Choose one of the paths leading from each decision box as determined by the site conditions. The most critical factors are listed first, and may constitute a simple go/no-go decision. For example, using wheeled skidders on fine-textured soils with high moisture content is not recommended. The factors further down in the chart typically have more feasible outcomes — follow the path that most closely

**Table 7.** *Risk factors applicable to all harvesting equipment*

| Factor | Comment |
|---|---|
| Operator experience, attitude, and history | Risk is decreased with an experienced operator who has worked successfully under similar conditions in the past, and has demonstrated a desire to do a proper job. |
| Contractor experience, attitude, and history | Risk is decreased with an experienced contractor who has worked successfully under similar conditions in the past, and has demonstrated a desire to do a proper job. Effective communications between the planners and the workers and adequate supervision decrease the risk of a mishap caused by misunderstood instructions. |
| Weather | Inclement weather, especially excessive rainfall, increases the risk. The risk of causing soil disturbance increases with higher soil moisture content. Maintaining a flexible schedule, with the ability to work on different areas as required by weather conditions, reduces the risk. |
| Sensitive zones | Working in the vicinity of riparian zones, or other sensitive zones, increases the risk. Operators should always take extra care when working in sensitive zones. |
| Tree size | Risk is minimized when the tree size is matched to machine size. Trees that are too small decrease productivity and increase costs, while trees that are too large can overwork the machine, causing mechanical failure or environmental damage. |
| Timber quality | Risk is increased with poor-quality timber because of reduced values. Poor-quality timber requires as much, or more, time for processing, yet returns a smaller profit. |

describes the site characteristic. Proceed through the chart until you arrive at a risk-level box.

In some cases, a first-mentioned factor on the chart may result in a high, but non-limiting, risk level (e.g., in Chart 15, non-clearcuts are ranked as risk level 4). On the same chart, another factor may be ranked with a higher risk level (e.g., poor deflection is ranked as risk level 6). This result should not be interpreted as saying that poor deflection in a non-clearcut will result in risk level 4. Obviously, the higher risk level will prevail.

Comments at the bottom of each chart list additional factors that apply for all types of sites, and should be considered in assessing the risk level. Table 7 lists risk factors that should be considered for all types of equipment. Finally, the contractor and operator may employ special operating techniques that can modify the risk levels.

# Key Factors for Primary Transport Equipment

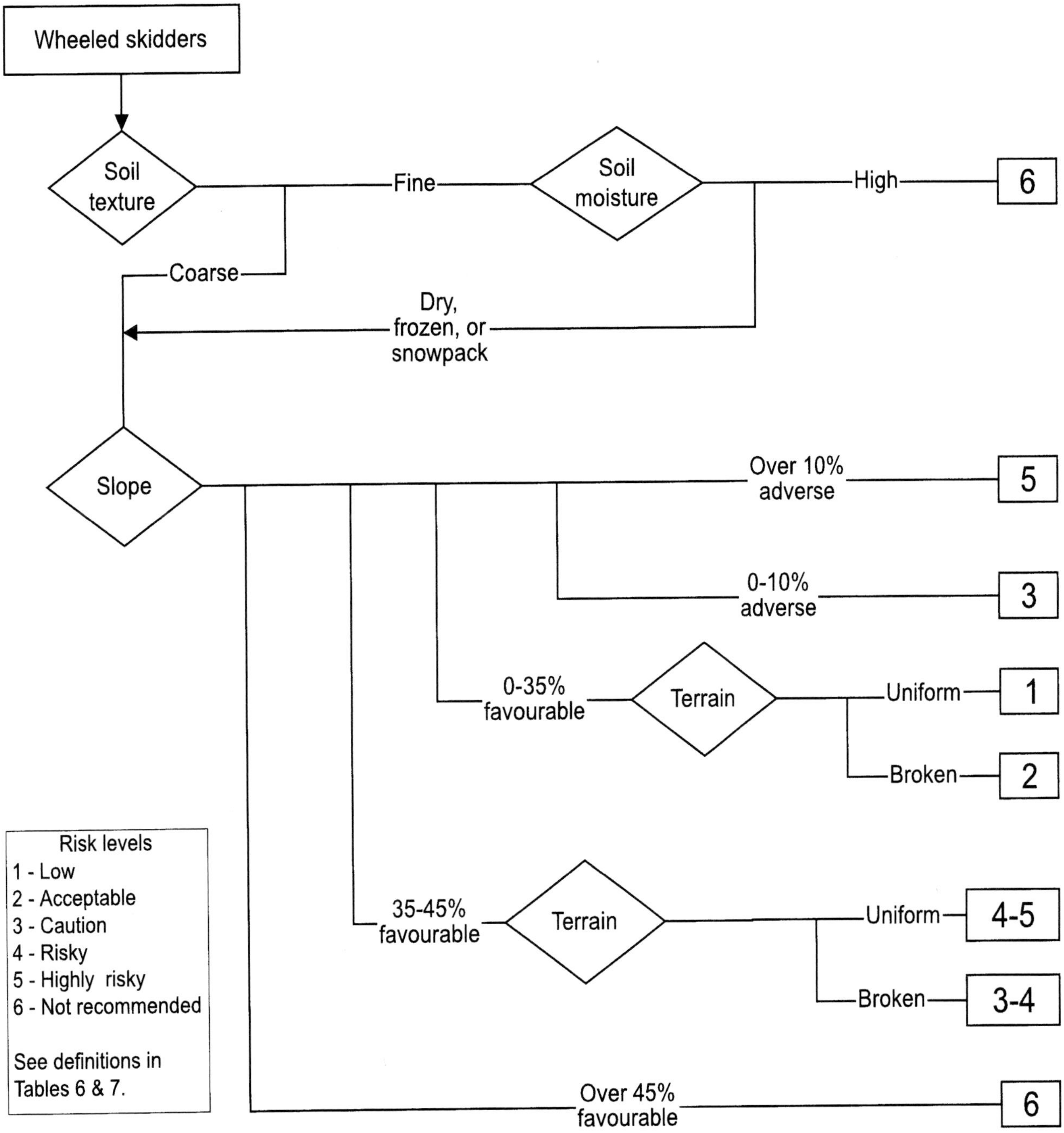

**Wheeled skidders**

- Soil texture
  - Fine → Soil moisture
    - High → **6**
    - Dry, frozen, or snowpack → (to Slope)
  - Coarse → (to Slope)

- Slope
  - Over 10% adverse → **5**
  - 0-10% adverse → **3**
  - 0-35% favourable → Terrain
    - Uniform → **1**
    - Broken → **2**
  - 35-45% favourable → Terrain
    - Uniform → **4-5**
    - Broken → **3-4**
  - Over 45% favourable → **6**

**Risk levels**
1 - Low
2 - Acceptable
3 - Caution
4 - Risky
5 - Highly risky
6 - Not recommended

See definitions in Tables 6 & 7.

## Chart 1. Wheeled skidders.

- The ability to turn skidders safely is reduced on steep slopes. The presence of large obstacles such as boulders, depressions, or windfalls will increase the risk, especially on steep slopes, because they increase the difficulty of turning around the machine. Benches may increase the opportunity for turning safely. Obstacles also reduce the travel speed and increase the travel distance.

- Grapple skidders are best suited for use with mechanical falling and bunching equipment, which requires that the tree size be within the operating range of the falling equipment. Grapple skidders enable roadside operations, which can reduce production costs. Swing-boom grapples reduce the risk on steep ground. On wetter sites, line skidders can drop their load and move forward to more firm terrain before winching the load, thus reducing the risk of soil disturbance.

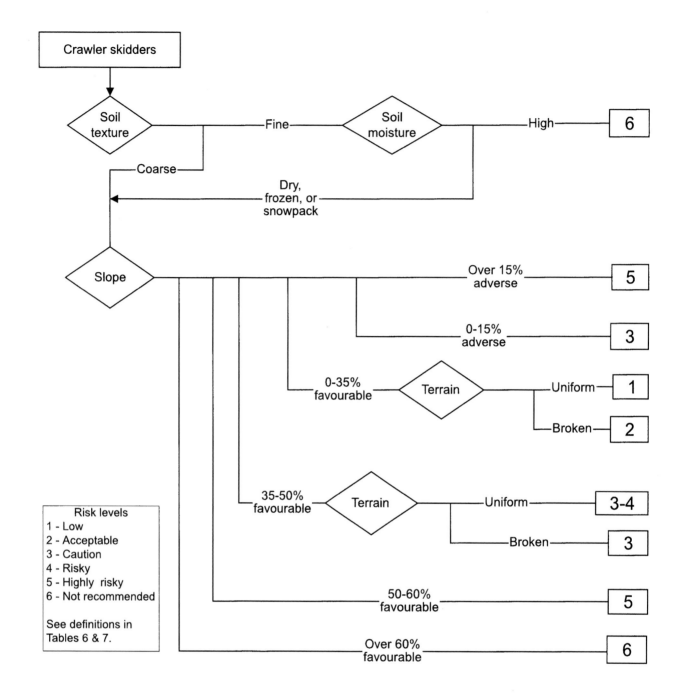

**Chart 2. Crawler skidders.**

- The ability to turn skidders safely is reduced on steep slopes. The presence of large obstacles such as boulders, depressions, or windfalls will increase the risk, especially on steep slopes, because they increase the difficulty of turning around the machine. Benches may increase the opportunity for turning safely. Obstacles also reduce the travel speed and increase the travel distance.

- Grapple skidders are best suited for use with mechanical falling and bunching equipment, which requires that the tree size be within the operating range of the falling equipment. Grapple skidders enable roadside operations, which can reduce production costs. Swing-boom grapples reduce the risk on steep ground. On wetter sites, line skidders can drop their load and move forward to more firm terrain, thus reducing the risk of soil disturbance.

- Low travel speed makes crawler skidders more suited to short skidding distances.

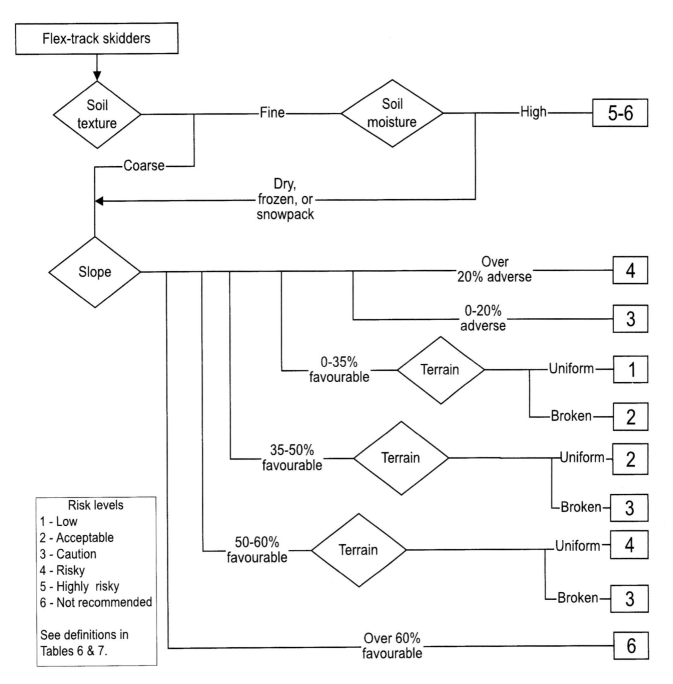

**Chart 3. Flex-track skidders.**

- The ability to turn skidders safely is reduced on steep slopes. The presence of large obstacles such as boulders, depressions, or windfalls will increase the risk, especially on steep slopes, because they increase the difficulty of turning around the machine. Benches may increase the opportunity for turning safely. Obstacles also reduce the travel speed and increase the travel distance.

- Grapple skidders are best suited for use with mechanical falling and bunching equipment, which requires that the tree size be within the operating range of the falling equipment. Grapple skidders enable roadside operations, which can reduce production costs. Swing-boom grapples reduce the risk on steep ground. On wetter sites, line skidders can drop their load and move forward to more firm terrain, thus reducing the risk of soil disturbance.

- The tracks for flex-track machines conform more closely to the ground profile than for conventional tracked skidders. This feature distributes their weight more evenly, allowing them to operate on soft ground and up adverse slopes with less soil disturbance.

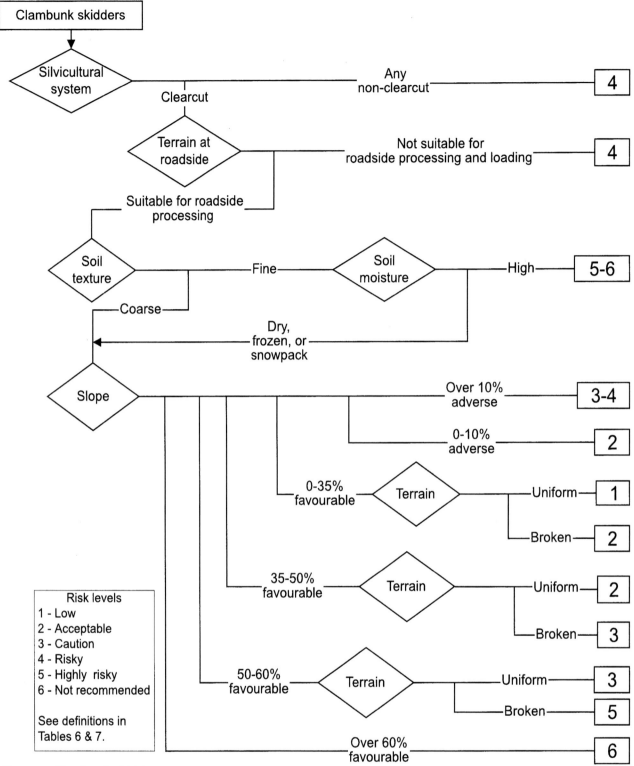

**Chart 4. Clambunk skidders.**

- The presence of large obstacles such as boulders, depressions, or windfalls will increase the risk because they reduce the travel speed and increase the travel distance.

- The risk level increases for low volumes per trail (i.e., for "shallow" or low volume per hectare cutblocks). The clambunk will be unable to obtain a full load, making it uneconomic to operate unless the skidding pattern is altered to attain full loading.

- Clambunks are best suited for use with mechanical falling and bunching, which requires that the tree size be within the operating range of the falling equipment.

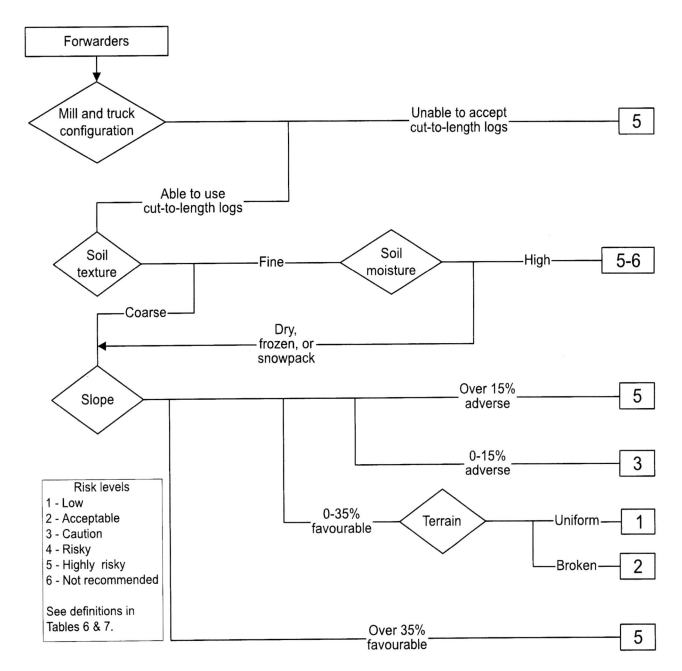

**Chart 5. Forwarders.**

- The risk level is very high if the mill and truck fleet are unable to accept cut-to-length logs, although these limitations are imposed by business requirements, not by the site characteristics. Timber sales to other companies and other options for transporting the logs should be considered.

- Large obstacles such as boulders, depressions, or windfalls will increase the risk because they reduce the travel speed and increase the travel distance.

- The tree size must be suitable for the feller-processor that works with the forwarder. Large trees may require falling and processing with additional equipment.

- Depending on machine size, the high degree of maneuverability between standing trees makes forwarders well suited to partial cutting operations.

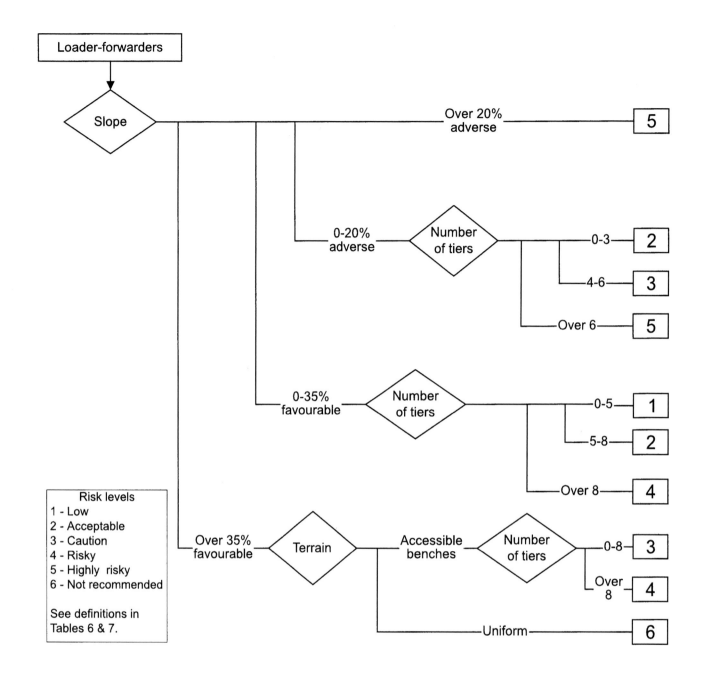

**Chart 6. Loader-forwarders.**

- Distance for each "tier" or "chuck" will vary depending on the size of the machine, the length of the timber, and the decision to buck trees into log lengths.

- The risk level increases for wet or fine soils and for small trees.

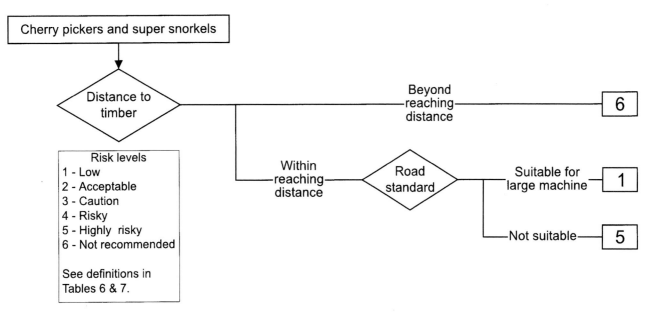

**Chart 7. Cherry pickers and super snorkels.**

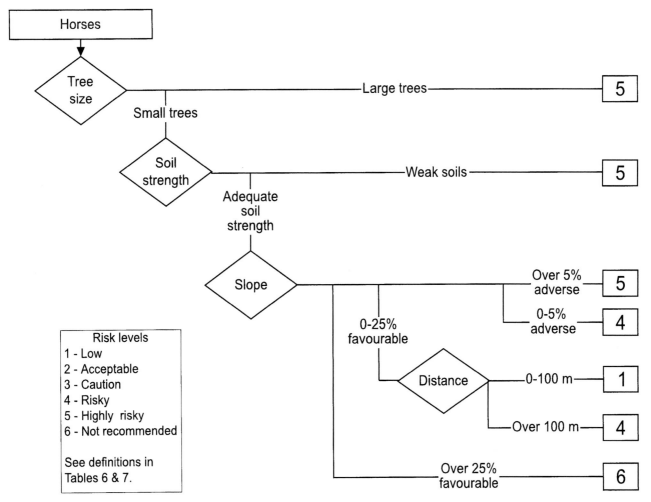

**Chart 8. Horse.**

- Skidding with horses is enhanced on a snowpack because of reduced friction. Risk increases for slopes over 15% under frozen conditions because of the potential for logs to slide downhill and strike the horse.

- The trails where the horses walk must be cleared of debris before skidding.

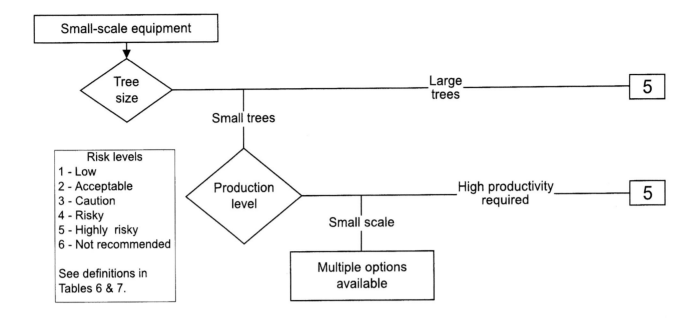

**Chart 9. Small-scale equipment.**

- Many types of small-scale equipment are available with a wide range of capabilities and key factors. They are used in niche applications, typically where tree size is small and productivity is low. Beyond that, examine the specific type of equipment proposed to determine whether it is usable.

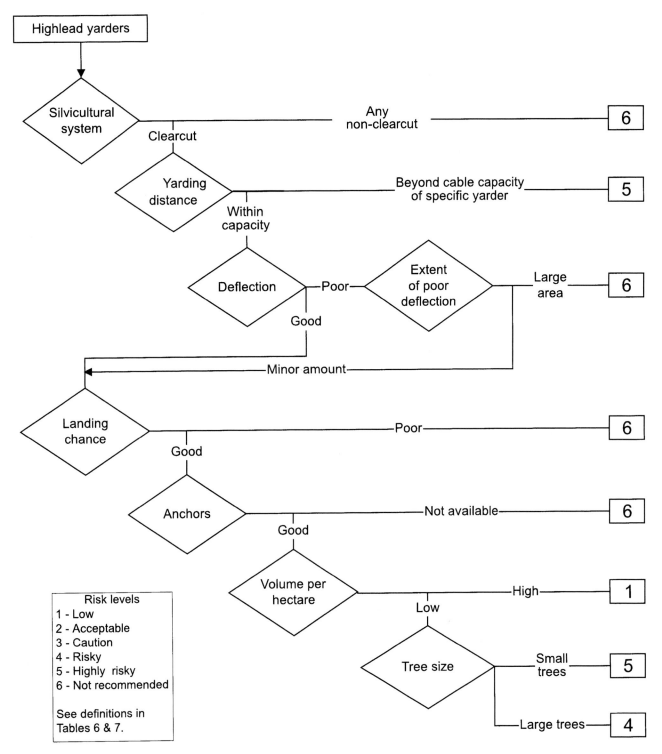

**Chart 10. Highlead yarders.**

- Highlead yarders can continue to work even if the butt-rigging drags on the ground, although this practice may result in excessive soil disturbance and low productivity.

- Landing chance refers to the ability to build and use suitable landings. Poor landing chance may be caused by difficult terrain or by the combination of terrain, deflection, and the tower location within the landing.

- Tree size and volume per hectare must be evaluated in relation to the specific machine, with a minimum economic volume ranging from 150 to 350 m³/ha depending on machine size.

- Anchors may consist of large tree stumps, several smaller trees or stumps, or fabricated anchors such as a buried log or rock bolts.

- Cable extensions can be used to reach logs beyond the yarder's normal working distance.

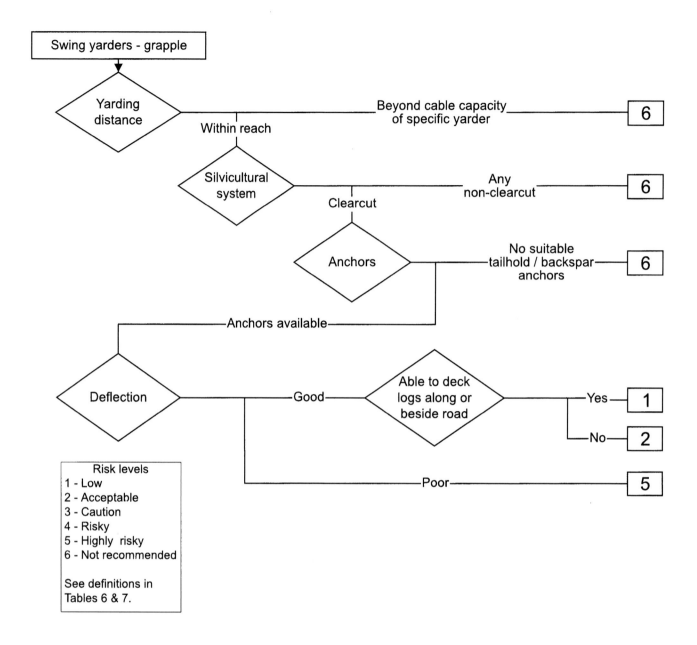

**Chart 11. Swing yarders – grapple.**

- The risk level is increased where mobile backspars cannot be used — conventional anchors must be available in their place. Anchors may consist of large tree stumps, several smaller trees or stumps, or fabricated anchors such as a buried log or rock bolts.

- The risk level increases for small tree size because the trees are picked up individually. Mechanical falling and bunching can reduce the risk.

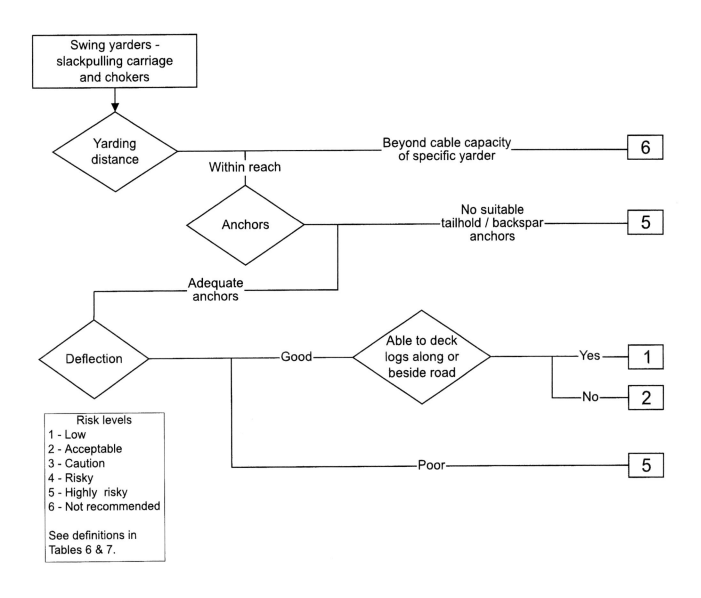

**Chart 12. Swing yarders – slackpulling carriage and chokers.**

- Anchors may consist of large tree stumps, several smaller trees or stumps, or fabricated anchors such as a buried log or rock bolts.

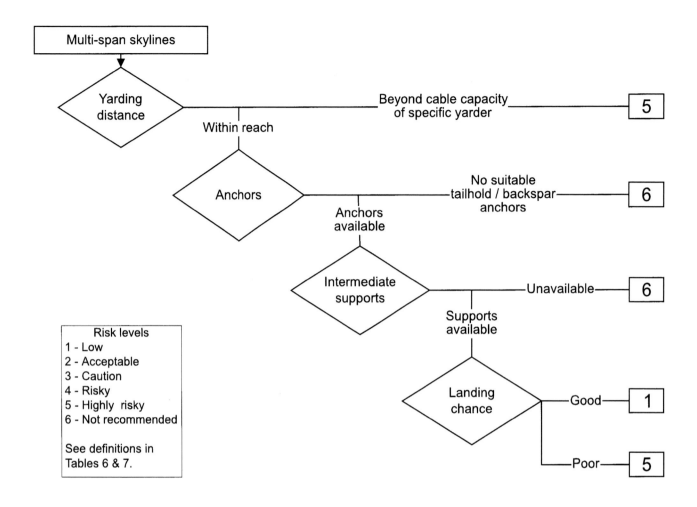

**Chart 13. Multi-span skylines.**

- Landing chance refers to the ability to build and use suitable landings for extraction and subsequent phases. Poor landing chance may be caused by difficult terrain or by the combination of terrain, deflection, and the tower location within the landing.

- Risk level increases as the volume per hectare decreases.

- Although intermediate supports allow for yarding in areas of poor deflection, risk increases as the number of intermediate supports increases.

- Payloads can be lifted over intervening obstacles depending on the ground profile, the layout, and the equipment capability.

- Anchors may consist of large tree stumps, several smaller trees or stumps, or fabricated anchors such as a buried log or rock bolts.

- Cable extensions can be used to reach logs beyond the yarder's normal working distance.

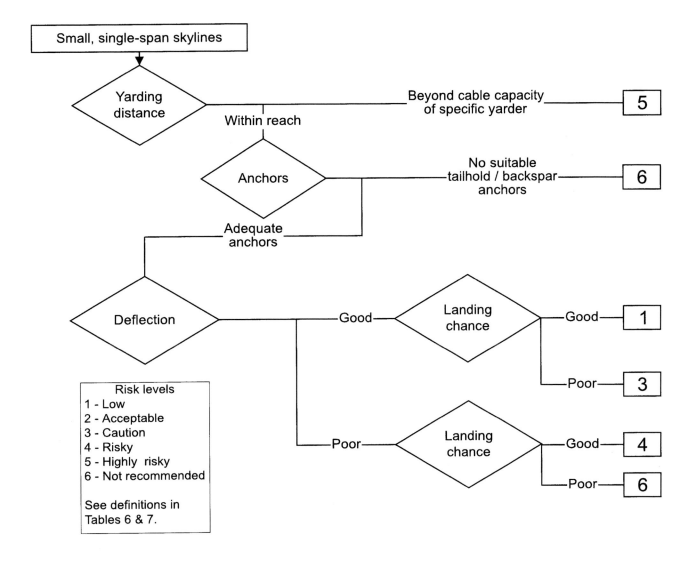

**Chart 14. Small, single-span skylines.**

- Landing chance refers to the ability to build and use suitable landings for extraction and subsequent phases. Poor landing chance may be caused by difficult terrain or by the combination of terrain, deflection, and the tower location within the landing.

- Risk level increases as the volume per hectare decreases.

- Payloads can be lifted over intervening obstacles, depending on deflection and clearance.

- Anchors may consist of large tree stumps, several smaller trees or stumps, or fabricated anchors such as a buried log or rock bolts.

- Cable extensions can be used to reach logs beyond the yarder's normal working distance.

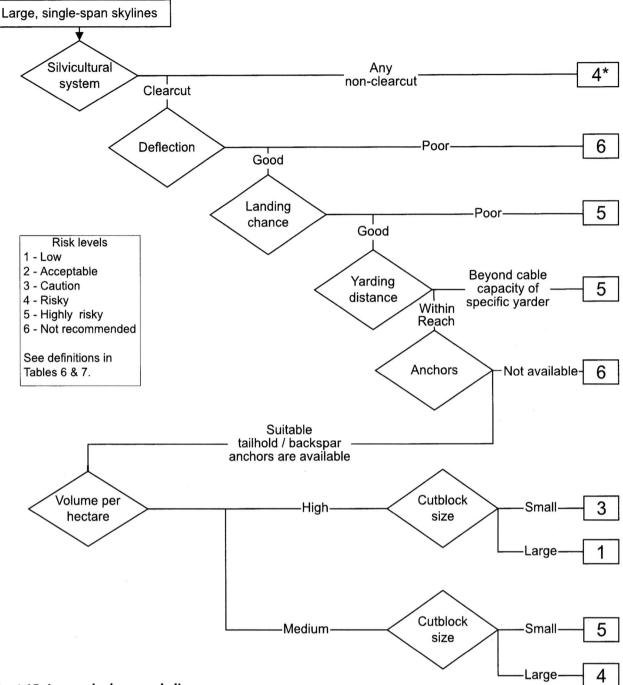

**Chart 15. Large, single-span skylines.**

* • The term "large" refers both to the yarder size and the skyline span — large tower-mounted yarders and European cable cranes both qualify as "large." However, the European cable cranes are better able to operate in non-clearcut silvicultural systems, and their risk would be lower than shown in the chart.

• Landing chance refers to the ability to build and use suitable landings for extraction and subsequent phases. Poor landing chance may be caused by difficult terrain or by the combination of terrain, deflection, and the tower location within the landing.

• Payloads can be lifted over intervening obstacles depending on deflection and clearance.

• Risk increases with too-large deflection because of the increased time required for the chokers to travel between the carriage and the ground.

• Anchors may consist of large trees or stumps, or fabricated anchors such as a buried log or rock bolts.

• Cable extensions can be used to reach logs beyond the yarder's normal working distance.

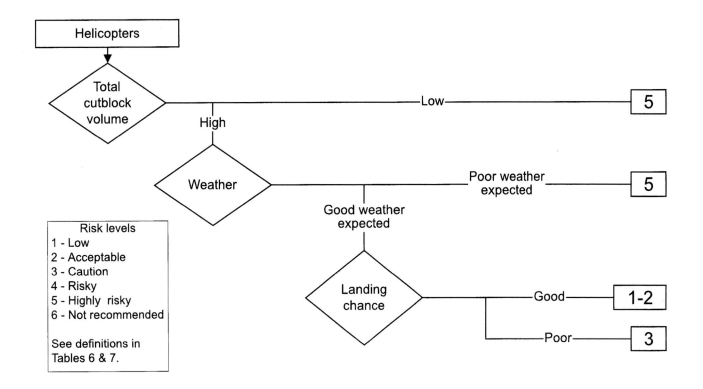

**Chart 16. Helicopters.**

- Suitable landings are large enough to handle the expected volume of logs without causing delays. Flying, processing, storage, and loading must all be accommodated. A separate landing for helicopter fueling and maintenance is required.

- Risk level increases when multiple hookup sites are not available, with long flying distances, and with adverse or very steep favourable slope between the hookup site and the landing.

- Poor weather such as high wind or reduced visibility can affect the ability of the helicopter to fly safely.

- Payloads can be lifted over intervening obstacles.

# Key Factors for Falling Equipment

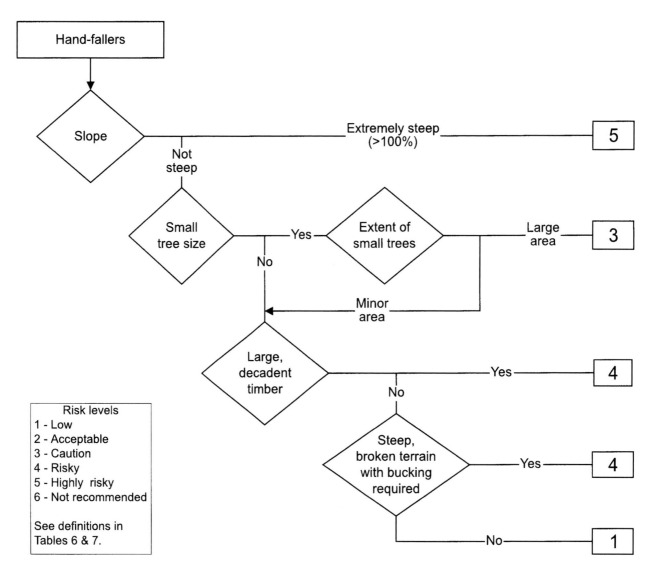

**Chart 17. Hand-fallers.**

- Hand-fallers can work on almost any site, within the limits of economics and safety.

- Falling small trees by hand is expensive, especially after considering the costs for extraction. Except with very small trees, hand-fallers are unable to build bunches.

- Hand-falling in decadent timber and bucking timber on steep, broken terrain are especially hazardous.

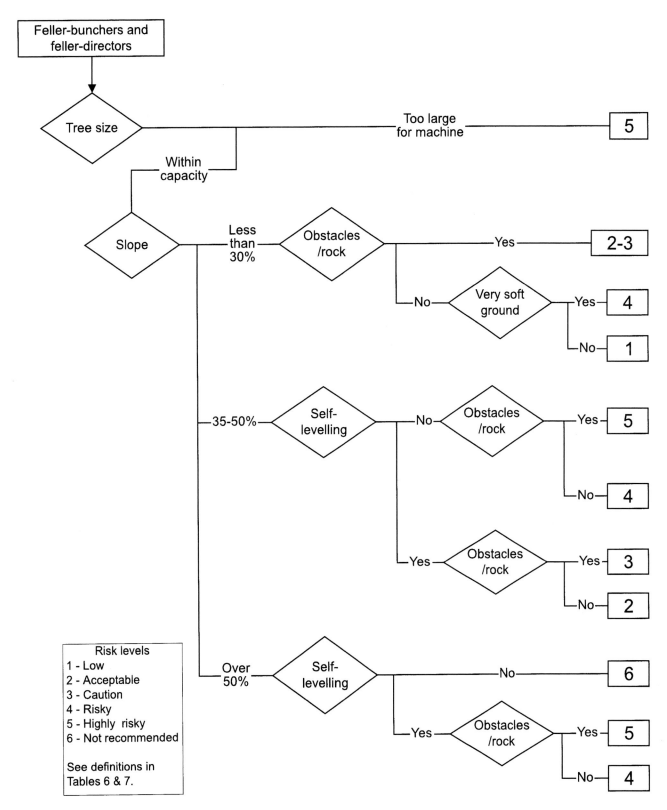

**Chart 18. Feller-bunchers and feller-directors.**

- Maximum tree size depends on the make and model of the carrier and head. Typical maximum tree diameter is about 60 cm, although larger heads up to 75 cm are available. Larger trees can be cut by approaching the tree from two or more sides.

- Feller-directors can handle larger trees than feller-bunchers, but they are poorly suited to making bunches.

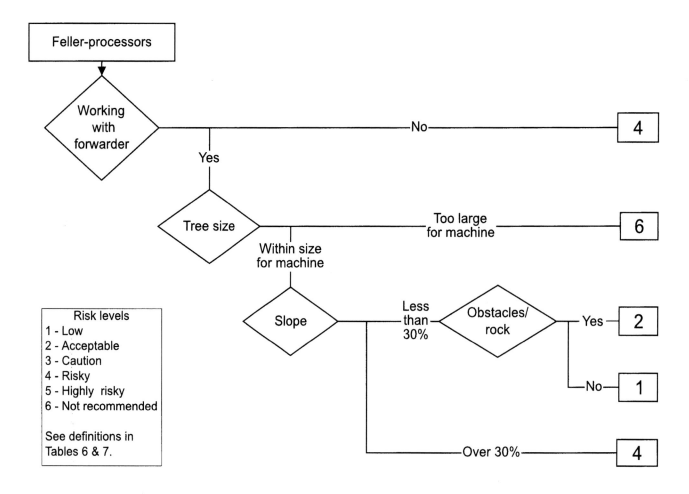

**Chart 19. Feller-processors.**

- This chart applies to feller-processors mounted on articulated, rubber-tired carriers. Use the "feller-buncher" chart for single-grip feller-processors mounted on excavator-style carriers.

- The maximum tree diameter for current single-grip feller-processors is about 50 cm. Current double-grip feller-processors can handle trees to about 65 cm diameter.

- Feller-processors must be able to accurately and reliably measure log lengths.

# Key Factors for Processing Equipment

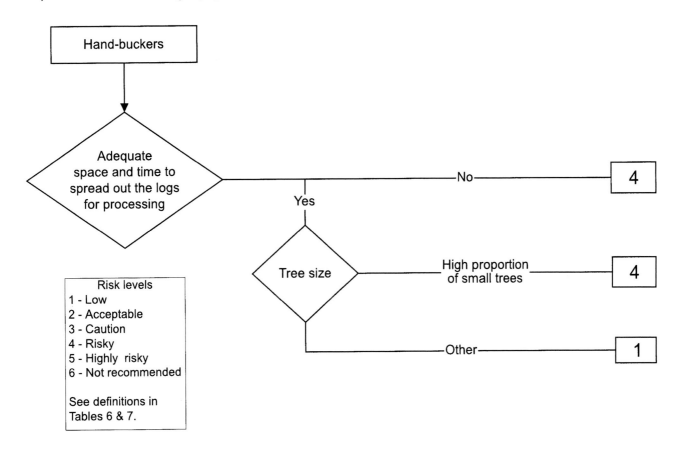

**Risk levels**
1 - Low
2 - Acceptable
3 - Caution
4 - Risky
5 - Highly risky
6 - Not recommended

See definitions in
Tables 6 & 7.

## Chart 20. Hand-buckers.

- Hand-bucking can be used on almost any site, within the constraints of safety and economics. Since hand-buckers require support equipment to move the logs, the bucker and support equipment must be able to work together safely. This requires adequate time between cycles of the loading or skidding equipment, and adequate space to spread out the logs for the bucker to examine and cut each log. Such conditions may be impossible to achieve on sites with a high proportion of small trees.

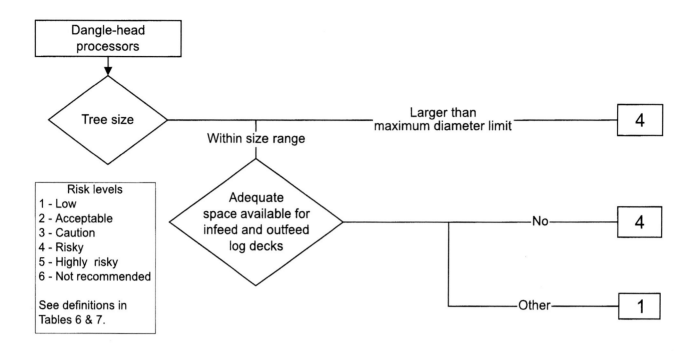

## Chart 21. Dangle-head processors.

- Dangle-head processors are typically used for smaller trees, with a maximum diameter of about 50 cm; however, some models can process logs up to 80 cm diameter. Trees larger than the rated maximum diameter can be handled by grasping the tree above the butt, where the diameter is smaller. Trees can also be left lying on the ground, and the processing head passed over them without actually lifting the tree.

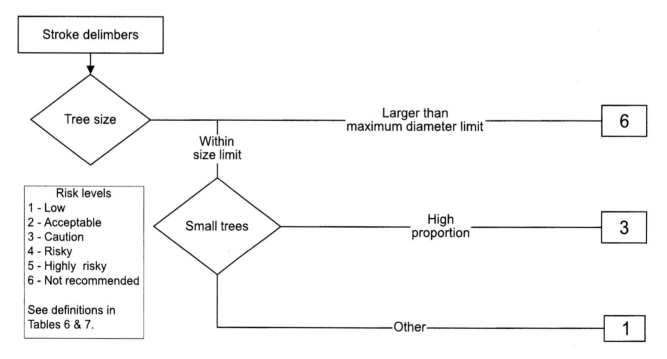

## Chart 22. Stroke delimbers.

- The maximum tree size for stroke delimbers is governed by the diameter of the tunnel through the machine — the trees must be able to fit through the tunnel.

- Stroke delimbers are less efficient for small trees than dangle-head processors because they pass over each log twice to complete the processing cycle. However, stroke delimbers can process several small trees simultaneously.

# Key Factors for Loading Equipment

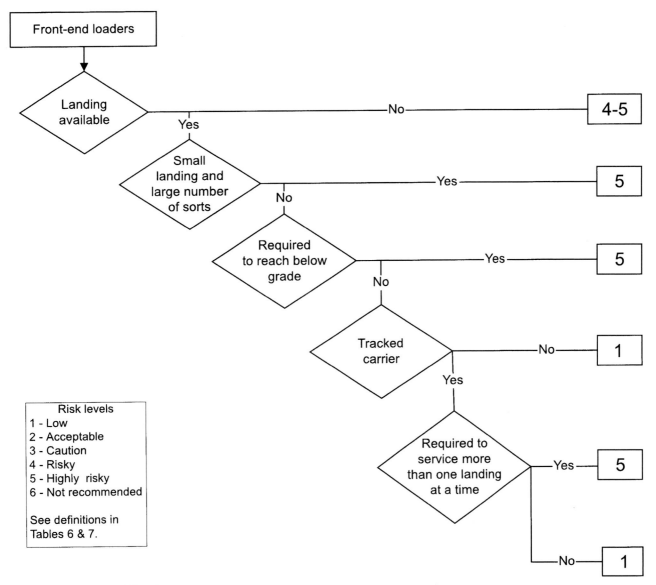

**Front-end loaders**

Landing available — No — **4-5**

Yes

Small landing and large number of sorts — Yes — **5**

No

Required to reach below grade — Yes — **5**

No

Tracked carrier — No — **1**

Yes

Required to service more than one landing at a time — Yes — **5**

No — **1**

Risk levels
1 - Low
2 - Acceptable
3 - Caution
4 - Risky
5 - Highly risky
6 - Not recommended

See definitions in Tables 6 & 7.

**Chart 23. Front-end loaders.**
- Wheeled front-end loaders can be moved quickly between sites several kilometres apart. Loaders on tracked carriers require low-bed transportation.

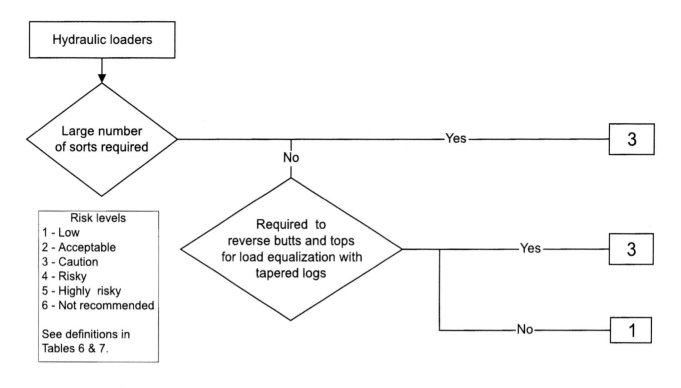

**Chart 24. Hydraulic loaders.**

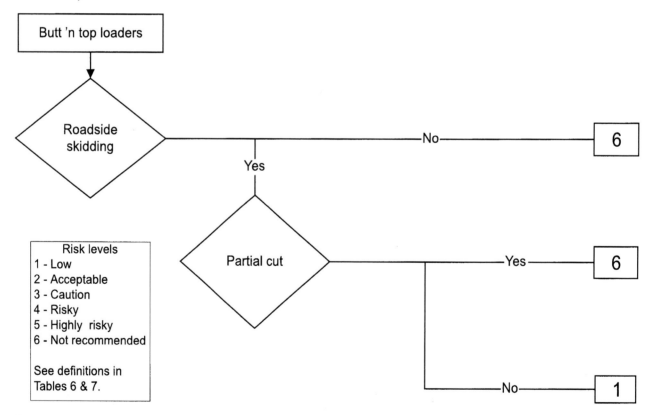

**Chart 25. Butt 'n top loaders.**

- Suitability of a cutblock for roadside logging is often determined by the ability of the butt 'n top loader to operate adjacent to the road. Sideslopes must be low enough for the loader to operate safely.

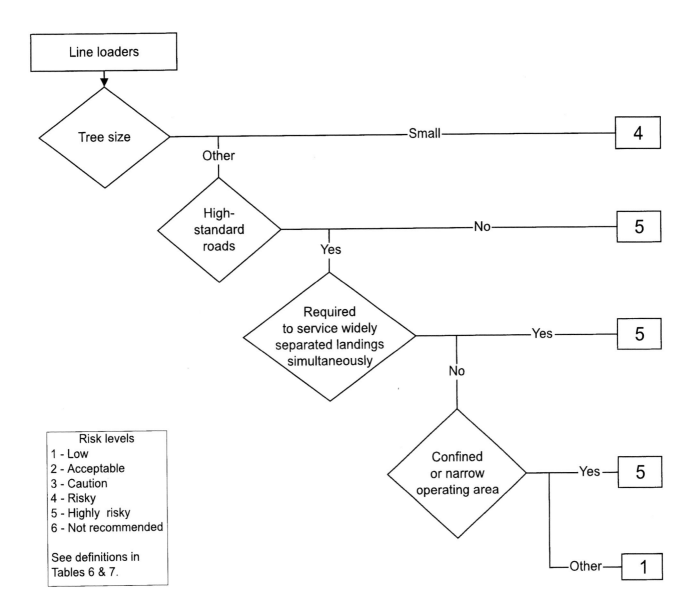

Risk levels
1 - Low
2 - Acceptable
3 - Caution
4 - Risky
5 - Highly risky
6 - Not recommended

See definitions in
Tables 6 & 7.

**Chart 26. Line loaders.**

- Line loaders can be moved relatively easily between loading sites up to several hundred metres apart, and are often used to service two towers simultaneously. Landings further apart pose difficulty for simultaneous operation because of low travel speeds, especially for track-mounted loaders. Low-bed transportation over longer distances is required. Rubber-mounted loaders can travel farther under their own power, but travel remains slow.

## EXAMPLES

These examples demonstrate how information can be obtained from the handbook to help match equipment to the site. The examples have been based on hypothetical scenarios that could be encountered by industrial or agency planners.

These examples illustrate that the handbook's purpose is to identify issues and concerns, and to evaluate the risks associated with combinations of site conditions and equipment. The handbook is not meant to provide the single "correct" answer about what equipment is suited to any particular site.

### Example 1: Change Harvest Season

A cutblock has been planned and approved for winter harvesting, but corporate log-flow requirements have made it important to advance the harvesting schedule, perhaps to late summer or early fall. What are the important issues that must be addressed with harvesting the cutblock earlier in the season? Will the same equipment be suitable? If not, what different equipment or operating techniques will achieve acceptable results?

The cutblock is proposed for clearcut harvesting, using typical roadside equipment comprising a feller-buncher, grapple skidders, stroke delimbers, and butt 'n top loader. The timber is small-diameter pine on rolling terrain, and the roads were laid out for a maximum of 250 m skidding. The maximum sideslope is about 30% and the soils are fine-textured. The proposed plan specifies harvesting under dry or frozen conditions.

Scan the column labelled "wheeled skidder - grapple" in Table 2 to determine what impacts could result from the proposed change to the harvesting schedule. Wheeled skidders require high soil strength, and have low to moderate ability to avoid ground disturbance, especially when the soil moisture content is high.

**Figure 1**
*Rubber-tired skidders may be a high-risk option for non-frozen conditions unless weather conditions are favourable.*

Chart 1 confirms this — operating on fine-textured soils under wet conditions is rated at risk level 6 (Table 6). Clearly, soil disturbance will be a significant concern.

The requirements and limitations of the skidding equipment will not be changed under a different harvesting schedule, so the planner must evaluate the risk of operating under non-frozen conditions. What is the likelihood of experiencing a period of sustained dry weather when the skidders may be able to operate successfully? If the likelihood of dry weather is low, resulting in a high risk of soil disturbance, then changes to the operating techniques or equipment will be required. Information listed in the Index under "soil disturbance - compaction - skidder" and "soil disturbance - rutting" describe wide tires and devices to fit over the skidder tires to reduce their ground pressure. These devices could reduce the risk of causing soil disturbance.

However, the rubber-tired skidder remains a high-risk option even with tracks or wide tires, so alternative equipment should be considered. Clambunks, forwarders, loader-forwarders, small-scale equipment, and horse logging are the ground-based options with greater ability to avoid ground disturbance (Table 2). The latter two options are high risk for this scenario because of their low productivity. Although the forwarder is less susceptible to high soil moisture, it could be high risk because it requires specialized trucks and mill configuration (Chart 5) that may not be available. Specialized falling and loading equipment will also be required. Clambunks (Index: clambunk) may be better suited to the soil conditions than the skidders. Loader-forwarding could be an option, but the small timber size and long skidding distances increase the risk. Flex-track skidders are also rated in Table 2 with a low–moderate ability to avoid ground disturbance, but their risk on moist, fine-textured soils is rated slightly lower than skidders (Chart 3). They may be worth considering.

Cable equipment may provide an alternative more suited to reducing soil disturbance, but higher operating costs will increase the risk. Furthermore, the yarder must be suitable for roadside operations to fit with the processing and loading equipment, eliminating highlead yarders from consideration. The small tree size eliminates large equipment, although bunching could help to reduce the risk. Adequate deflection and clearance will be critical to avoid soil disturbance (Chart 14). Rolling terrain with maximum 30% sideslopes over yarding distances of 250 m will make it difficult to achieve adequate clearance with a short yarder. Multi-span skylines could be considered.

The only alternatives to the wheeled skidder that seem viable are the clambunk skidder and the flex-track skidder. The forwarder may be viable if the corporate infrastructure supports shortwood logging.

Clearly, any equipment changes required in this scenario will be short term, and therefore must be confined to equipment that is readily available for hire. Most of the alternative equipment is capital-intensive (Table 1), and is likely to be gainfully employed and unavailable for a short-term rental. Furthermore, all the alternatives are more expensive than the original proposal — the planner must evaluate the benefit of the altered harvesting schedule with the added costs.

## Example 2: Review Development Plan

As a Small Business forester for the British Columbia Ministry of Forests, you are responsible for preparing forest development plans for the Small Business Forest Enterprise Program. An area of your development plan includes a coastal cutblock where the layout contractor has proposed skyline yarding over a creek. You are unfamiliar with skyline systems, and want to ensure that the proposed harvesting will achieve all the operational and environmental objectives. What are the issues that should be addressed in your review? What alternatives should be considered?

The cutblock is located in an incised valley with sideslopes averaging about 70%, although the sideslope reaches about 100% at the higher elevations. A road was constructed about 15 years ago to harvest the timber on one side of the creek using a grapple yarder. The cutblock was reforested after harvesting, and now supports a stand of trees about 5–7 m tall. The timber on the far side of the valley was not harvested because of difficult terrain. It has numerous rock bluffs dispersed throughout the standing timber, which would result in extremely expensive road construction. A narrow band of trees left adjacent to the creek after the original harvesting has not sustained any significant amount of windthrow. A similar buffer strip is proposed for the far side of the creek. Two landings are proposed on the existing road for skyline yarding, and the maximum distance from the landings to the cutblock boundary is about 700 m.

**Figure 2**
*Large skyline towers
can suspend logs over
streams providing the
conditions are suitable*

Table 2 indicates that the proposed large, single-span skyline will adequately address any concerns about soil disturbance, but the cross-stream yarding concerns you with the possibility of introducing debris into the stream. Will the skyline be able to lift the logs clear of the buffer strip? Chart 15 indicates that deflection is a primary consideration for large skylines, and the Index points to several areas with information about deflection. Clearly, both deflection and clearance are important, so you make a note to ask the layout contractor for representative deflection lines. You will ask about the amount of deflection, and the amount of clearance below the carriage. You also note to ask whether the trees will be yarded full-length, or will they be bucked beforehand? This will affect the required amount of clearance over the standing trees. You learned from the information under "hand-falling" and "hand-bucking" that on-site bucking is difficult and dangerous in such steep terrain. If clearance is inadequate, you will ask what plans have been made for corridors through the standing timber.

You also notice from Chart 15 that the landing chance and anchors are critical for successful skyline operations, so you will ask about the landings (Index: landing - yarding). The original harvesting was done by grapple yarders, which do not require landings, but the skyline yarders will need landings. Will the landings encroach on the plantation, and will they have adequate space to accommodate the yarding debris? What anchors are available at the landing to hold the tower (Index: anchor - guyline), and what anchors will be required at the tailholds? Will the anchors be located at the cutblock boundary, or will they be extended above the cutblock boundary to increase deflection (Index: anchor – backspar)?

You make another note to ask the layout contractor whether alternatives to cross-stream yarding have been considered. Clearly, ground-based systems are impractical because of the steep and difficult terrain (Table 2), but you want to ensure that all the options have been considered. Alternative yarding systems would involve building a road on the other side of the creek, so you make a note to ask whether a road survey was conducted on the far side, and if so, why it was not chosen for construction. You know from Chart 10 that highlead systems are more tolerant of poor landings than large skylines, so you will ask about potential landings on the alternative road location. You also know from the Index information on "yarding - slope - downhill" that safety in the landing is a major concern.

You also consider helicopter logging. You know from Table 1 and Table 2 that helicopter extraction is more expensive than skylines, but you want to ensure that all alternatives have been explored. You know from the descriptions of helicopters (Index: helicopter) that the helicopter must be matched in size to the timber resource and that bucking the trees by weight rather than by length is important. Bucking on the steep, broken ground may be difficult. Also, landing size and safety in the landing are major concerns — you note to ask whether helicopter logging was considered, and if so, what landing location would be used.

Armed with your new knowledge about skylines, you feel more confident that you can ask pertinent questions about the proposed system, and any alternatives that were considered.

## Example 3: Encounter New Operating Conditions

XYZ Forest Products had been operating in consistent timber and terrain types for more than 10 years, but is now faced with new conditions as it moves into a different area. Previously, the average cutblock had been laid out for clearcut logging with roadside processing, but the planners for XYZ realize this system is unsuitable for the new operating area. The slopes are steeper, and visual-quality objectives make large clearcuts unacceptable. Partial cutting will be required. The timber size is about the same, although the soils are generally of finer texture.

XYZ has four contractors, each producing about 120 000 m³/yr in roadside operations for a total of 480 000 m³/yr. The total cut for the operating division will be reduced to about 450 000 m³/yr, with the new area comprising about 50 000 m³/yr. One option among several being considered is to retain three contractors at their current levels, and to reduce one of the contractors to 90 000 m³/yr, working in a combination of the new and existing operating areas.

The company, and its contractors, must determine whether the equipment that was used previously will be acceptable for the new operating area.

Three of the contractors have very similar equipment: two feller-bunchers, two grapple skidders, two stroke delimbers, and one butt 'n top loader. Each of the contractors has at least one levelling-cab feller-buncher, and all of the feller-bunchers are equipped with high-speed disc saws. The fourth contractor has different equipment: two feller-bunchers, but neither have levelling cabs, one grapple skidder that is used as required, one clambunk skidder, two dangle-head processors, and a butt 'n top loader.

What is the best equipment allocation for the new area?

The new operating conditions have five critical differences: steeper terrain, finer-textured soils, partial cutting, less operating volume, and the requirement for flexibility between the new and old operating conditions. Taking these in order, Table 2 indicates that wheeled skidders are best suited to slopes less than 35%. Depending on the amount of area over 35% or over 50%, the wheeled skidders may be marginally suited or completely unsuited to the new conditions (Chart 1). Furthermore, the requirement for partial cutting makes grapple-based equipment poorly suited because of its limited reach (Index: skidder - grapple).

**Figure 3**
*Clambunk skidders may be able to work on the steeper slopes of the new operating area.*

Will the clambunk skidder be any better suited? Table 2 indicates that clambunks can work on steeper terrain and require less soil strength, but there are three major factors that make clambunks poorly suited to this situation: they are grapple-based, they are large, and difficult to maneuver within a partial cut (Index: clambunk - partial cutting), and they require a large operating volume to make them cost-effective (Index: clambunk).

It appears that the present equipment fleet is not well suited to the new conditions. What features should the company and contractor be looking for in replacement equipment?

The steep terrain, fine-textured soils, partial cutting, and low operating volume will all be critical factors in the specification. Wheeled-based equipment may be unsuited, depending on the steepness of the terrain, even if operations could be confined to frozen or deep snowpack conditions to address the soil disturbance concerns. Track-based equipment would have better stability for improved safety. For grapple-equipped machines to work effectively, especially in partial cutting, they must be matched with suitable felling equipment (Index: skidder - grapple), which means that a zero-clearance feller-buncher with a levelling cab will likely be required (Index: feller-buncher – partial cutting). Without the appropriate falling equipment, line skidders will be required (Table 2).

Forwarders may be an option, depending on the terrain steepness, but the mill and trucking fleet must be configured to accept the different log specifications. Different felling equipment would also be required to manufacture the short logs.

Cable equipment should also be considered, but only carriage-based yarders because of the partial cutting (Table 2). With the projected volume (50 000 m³/yr), and typical daily production rates, year-round operations will be required. Costs may be prohibitive with the small trees unless feller-bunchers can be used. As before, a levelling cab will be required, but the soils must be examined carefully to ascertain if a feller-buncher can be used during the summer. Depending on the typical ground profiles and deflection, multi-span capabilities may be necessary (Chart 13, Chart 14, Index: deflection).

Processing and loading equipment must also be considered. The traditional operating area used roadside processing, but the new area will likely use landings because of the steeper terrain. The butt 'n top loaders will not be suited, although the processors can be used in roadside or landing configurations.

Lastly, the company and contractor must consider the overall effect of annual production levels. Under the scenario as presented, one contractor would be downsized to 90 000 m³ – 50 000 m³ from the new area and 40 000 m³ from the traditional operating areas. The previous equipment fleet was based on high-volume roadside logging, and will no longer be cost-effective. What equipment will be used on that area? The overall scenario seems unworkable, and should be reconsidered. The new operating area requires different types of equipment, but changes cannot be made without considering the impacts on the traditional operating areas.

As stated before, the purpose of this handbook is not to identify the single "correct" answer, but to identify issues that must be considered and how the characteristics of the various types of equipment address those issues. The preceding examples illustrate how to use the information in the handbook to improve equipment selection.

# Harvesting Systems and Equipment
## Part Two
**R E F E R E N C E**

Harvesting timber consists of several phases: falling the trees, manufacturing them into logs, and transporting the logs from the stump to a landing or roadside and then to a conversion facility. Many factors influence the exact sequence and details of these phases, but regardless of the details, the basic concept remains the same: harvesting timber consists of cutting trees and transporting them from one location to another. The operations are conducted sequentially, and the output of one phase becomes the input to the subsequent phase.

**Figure 4**
*A mid-sized skidder, typical of many ground-based operations in the Interior of British Columbia, working on a landing with a dangle-head processor.*

The most common method for classifying harvesting systems is to consider the primary transport phase; that is, from stump to the landing or roadside. Although usually the second phase in sequence, primary transport is discussed first in the handbook because of its importance.

The three basic classes of primary transport are ground-based, cable, and aerial. In ground-based harvesting systems, the logs are dragged or carried from the stump to the landing by a machine that travels over the ground. In cable systems, an overhead cable attached to a stationary machine is used to drag or carry the logs; in aerial systems, the logs are lifted above the ground by a machine that derives its lift from the air. This section of the handbook describes the defining features of these three classes of primary transport equipment.

**Figure 5**
*A mid-sized swing yarder.*

The features described here determine the generally accepted operating range of the equipment, but not necessarily the entire operating range. Some makes or models may include unique features used to extend the normal operating range. These unique design

**Figure 6**
*A heavy-lift helicopter used in coastal areas.*

features, or even special operating techniques, allow equipment to be operated outside of its normal operating range. While the handbook describes typical operating ranges, every situation should be examined on its own merit to determine the risk of using the proposed equipment under the expected site conditions.

## Common Features of Ground-based Equipment

Ground-based equipment travels from the landing or roadside to the stump and returns with a payload of logs. This process requires that roads be located within an acceptable skidding distance of the felling site, and that the site have terrain that is not too steep or broken and soils strong enough to support the machine.

### Machines travel across the ground to the cutting site

Since they simply drive over the ground, ground-based equipment can be less complex than either cable or aerial equipment. And since, by definition, they drive over the growing site, this equipment may affect the growing conditions.

**OPERATIONAL**

Less complex ground-based equipment is typically less costly to own and operate than either cable or aerial systems.

**ENVIRONMENTAL**

There is an inherent risk of soil damage from machine traffic.

Soil damage typically occurs when the machines travel over the same route several times, exceed the soil bearing strength (see soil bearing strength, following), and turn around at the felling site, landing, or roadside. Design features or operating techniques that reduce the risk of these occurrences are important to consider. For example, the turning action for tracked machines causes one track to skid over the ground which can cause soil disturbance. Some tracked machines have proportional steering between the tracks to reduce or eliminate the skidding effect when turning. Two operating strategies to reduce disturbance from turning are (1) to turn the machine only on debris, or (2) to back the machine from the landing to the felling site, and drive forward on the return trip. The latter strategy is commonly used for forwarders and clambunk skidders.

**Figure 7**
*A large grapple skidder operating from a landing in the Interior of British Columbia.*

Ground-based machines can drive between the residual stems in a partial cutting prescription. Unlike cable systems, a straight corridor is not required; however, a sufficient number of trees must be cut to allow the machine and its payload to pass without binding or breaking, or damaging residual trees.

Crossing streams with ground-based equipment may cause unacceptable disturbance, and must be strictly controlled. Temporary bridge crossings may provide one method for crossing the stream within allowable disturbance limits, and equipment such as forwarders can carry the bridge to the site and place it in position with minimal disturbance.

## Soil requires adequate load-bearing strength

Because the soil must support the machine and payload weight, inadequate soil strength can result in soil degradation such as compaction or rutting. In general, coarse, well-drained soils are stronger than fine-textured or moist soils. The soil's strength may be enhanced by frozen conditions, or the machine's weight can be distributed over a wider area by using wide tires, wide-track pads, flotation mats, woody debris, or deep snow to prevent damage to the soil.

On sites that are highly sensitive to soil compaction and puddling, it is common to schedule harvesting operations when the soil strength is greatest (i.e., under dry or frozen conditions), or to select harvesting systems other than ground-based.

**Figure 8**
*Wide tires reduce the ground pressure of this skidder.*

Operating in areas with soils with low load-bearing capacity may require different operating techniques such as operating only at certain times of the year, using wide tires, or using particular skidding patterns. These techniques are discussed later in the handbook.

### OPERATIONAL

Operating on soils with low load-bearing capacity will increase the cycle times because the machine may get stuck, its travel speed may be reduced, or its payload may be reduced. Maintenance costs will be increased because of increased wear and tear on the machine.

### ENVIRONMENTAL

Soil compaction and rutting can result from operating ground-based equipment on soils with low load-bearing capacity, which can lead to soil erosion or reduction in growing site.

## Suitable ground slope required

The ground slope must be within the safe operating range, which varies depending on the type of equipment. Typical maximum favourable slope limits for wheeled skidders are 35%, and tracked machines can work to about 50%. Some specialized tracked machines can operate on slopes up to 60%. The upper limit for loaders working as forwarders is about 25–35%.

Occupational safety rules may restrict the range of slopes for ground-based equipment. Check for regulations that may apply in the particular operating area or jurisdiction.

### OPERATIONAL

Ground-based equipment can become unstable on steep slopes, especially when turning. Small obstacles such as windfalls and stumps that can be negotiated safely on lesser slopes may cause the machine to overturn. When skidding downhill with line skidders on steep slopes, the logs may run ahead into the machine, thus presenting a safety hazard.

Skidders can travel in random patterns on gentle slopes, but require trails to be constructed on steeper slopes. Constructing and deactivating trails increase costs. Cycle times are increased on steep slopes.

ENVIRONMENTAL

Bladed skid trails are a potential source of sediment generation. Subsurface flow can be intercepted and concentrated by bladed skid trails, and become a way to transport sediment. Without site rehabilitation, skid trails may not become sufficiently restocked with desirable species.

## Roads required within skidding distance

The typical maximum skidding distance for wheeled equipment is approximately 200–300 m, although some machines can operate economically up to 800–1000 m. Track-mounted machines are typically economical for shorter distances below 200 m.

Distances of 800 m cannot usually be obtained within a single cutblock; instead, they often imply travel through "dead ground" that is not being harvested. An exception is forwarding from small patches — long-distance skidding equipment can be used to centralize the processing and loading in a single location rather than in each of the patches.

OPERATIONAL

The maximum skidding distances are determined by economics, not by physical limitations of the machines. Longer skid distances increase the cycle times and skidding costs, while shorter skidding distances reduce the skidding costs and increase the road density and the road-construction costs. Larger payloads can offset the effect of longer skidding distances because fewer cycles are required to transport the same volume of timber.

The relative effect of skidding distance on productivity varies according to the type of equipment, and is a function of travel speed, payload, and hookup and unhook times. Machines with fast hookup times and low payloads (e.g., grapple skidder) are most effective at short skidding distances. Conversely, machines with large payloads and longer loading and unloading times (e.g., line skidder) are more effective at longer distances. In Figure 9 (adapted from Plamondon and Favreau 1994), the productivity functions for grapple and line skidders cross at about 100 m skidding distance. The relative effectiveness of the two machines varies with distance.

**Figure 9**

*The relative advantage of different machines changes depending on the skidding distance.*

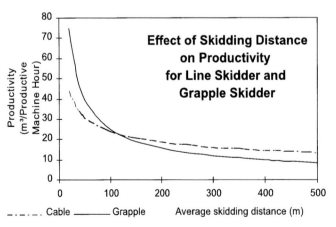

ENVIRONMENTAL

Short skidding distances increase the road density, which increases the potential for siltation and reduces the net area for restocking. Longer skidding distances reduce the road density, but can increase the soil compaction on skid trails. Longer skid distances can also increase the amount of soil compaction near the road because of increased traffic.

## Favourable travel surface required

Ground-based equipment requires that the ground surface be relatively uniform, and free from large, impassable obstacles. For example, large boulders, gullies, or stumps may hamper the machine's mobility.

**Figure 10**
*A forwarder working under nearly ideal conditions: the terrain is uniform, with no obstacles, and has only a slight adverse grade.*

However, broken ground can also enhance the mobility if the ground is interspersed with passable trails. For example, steep ground with benches can be harvested safely, especially if the timber can be felled towards the benches within the machine's reach. Short pitches of steep ground can be traversed safely.

### OPERATIONAL

Obstacles increase the cycle times and skidding costs, and can become hazards for overturning the machines. Every part of the cutblock must be close enough to a safe travel corridor for the machine to reach the logs.

### ENVIRONMENTAL

The potential for soil disturbance, erosion, or mass wasting caused by channelling water increases near gullies.

## Downhill skidding preferred

Ground-based equipment can usually skid downhill better than uphill; therefore, the truck road should be located in the lower portion of the cutblock. Short, steep pitches or sustained, gentle adverse slopes are acceptable. The amount of adverse grade that is acceptable depends on the type of machine.

### OPERATIONAL

Skidding on adverse slopes reduces travel speed and decreases productivity, and may require specialized equipment. The average skidding distance for a cutblock increases for a given road spacing because most of the skidding is from one side of the road only, instead of both sides as it would be for both adverse and favourable skidding.

### ENVIRONMENTAL

Spinning wheels or tracks on adverse skids can cause soil damage that can lead to increased siltation.

## Distinguishing Features of Ground-based Equipment

Three major features distinguish the various ground-based machines from one another: the machine type or method for transporting the trees or logs, the tractive system, and the machine size. An additional characteristic of skidders is the method used for holding the logs.

### Log transport method

Ground-based machines use several different methods for holding and transporting the logs: the method used defines the type of machine. The most common ground-based equipment is the skidder, which drags the logs behind itself while holding one end of the logs off the ground. The clambunk, a variation of the skidder, holds the logs in an inverted grapple. A second type is the forwarder, which carries the logs completely off the ground. A third type is the loader-forwarder, a loader that picks up the logs to swing or carry them a short distance. When log loaders are used from the haul road without travelling into the cutblock, they are usually called cherry pickers.

Horse logging or small-scale equipment such as chainsaw-powered winches or all-terrain vehicles are generally limited to smaller, niche operations.

Each of these types will be discussed in detail.

***Skidder*** Skidders are used for a wide range of applications, from the smallest operations to large, fully mechanized systems — various sizes suit different purposes. Skidders can be classified by their tractive system (rubber tires or tracks) and their method for holding the logs (chokers, grapple, or swing-boom grapple), as discussed later in detail.

**Figure 11**
*The skidder pushes the logs into a pile to keep the landing clear.*

In a typical work cycle, skidders travel from the landing or roadside to the felling site, turn around to hook the logs, and drag the logs to the destination. Depending on what other equipment is working in the system, the skidder may push the logs into larger piles to keep the landing area clear. Log breakage may result from rough handling with the skidder.

The weight of the logs is usually distributed unevenly between the front and rear of the machine, with the rear usually carrying a larger portion of the load. This results in increased ground pressure on the rear of the machine and adversely affects the machine's ability to skid uphill. Some skidders are specially designed to distribute the weight more evenly, thus improving their adverse skidding and ground pressure characteristics.

**Figure 12**
*A tracked skidder with a swing-boom grapple. The track frame is extended towards the rear of the machine to improve the balance.*

OPERATIONAL

Many contractors choose skidders because they are less expensive to own and operate, are versatile, and are well understood. Skidders are best suited to short to medium skidding distances. At longer distances (over 300–400 m), skidders become less economical to operate. The economically operable distance depends on travel speed and turn volumes — machines with faster cycle times or larger turn volumes can operate economically at longer distances.

Turning the machine around at the felling site on a steep sideslope is one of the most hazardous phases of the work cycle because skidders are unstable when positioned crossways on the slope. One technique to address this problem is to construct a trail to the top of the hill for returning to the work site. This allows the skidders to travel straight downhill over the steep ground. On broken ground, the skidders can turn on the benches and back up the hill for a short distance.

### ENVIRONMENTAL

Because of their low payloads, skidders require many trips over the same ground to harvest all the volume. This travel can lead to soil compaction on sensitive sites. Skidders may require bladed skid trails on steep ground, which can result in the loss of productive growing sites. In addition, skid trails may require rehabilitation after harvesting to restore the original ground slope and natural drainage patterns to reclaim the growing site and reduce the potential for soil erosion. On steep ground, the tracks caused by dragging the logs on the ground can become pathways for water to accumulate and flow.

*Clambunk* A clambunk resembles a large skidder with a log loader and grapple mounted on the rear of the machine. The grapple, which is mounted with the opening facing upwards, opens like a clamshell, thus deriving the machine's name.

**Figure 14**
*A clambunk skidder. Note the large, inverted grapple ("clambunk") and the tracks over the tires.*

In a typical work cycle, the clambunk travels in reverse from the roadside to the backline, eliminating the need to turn the machine around at either end of its cycle. Operators face the rear of the machine, looking over their shoulder when the machine travels forwards; the low travel speed makes this practical.

The butt ends of the logs are lifted into the grapple with the loader; when all the nearby logs have been loaded, the grapple is closed to secure the load. The machine travels forward to the next loading site, and the process is repeated until the grapple is full. Then the clambunk travels to the roadside to unload the logs, either by opening the grapple and driving out from under the load, or by using the log loader. The former technique is faster, but leaves the logs somewhat tangled for subsequent processing.

Clambunks usually have more axles than conventional skidders, and have a tire-and-track tractive system, so they can work on weaker soils.

### OPERATIONAL

Clambunks are large, slow-moving, and highly productive machines with large payloads and high ownership costs. Therefore, to minimize production costs, they are best suited to working with other high-production equipment such as feller-bunchers and mechani-

**Figure 15**
*A clambunk skidder operating on flat ground on the Interior Plateau.*

cal processors in a highly mechanized, roadside system. The high capital cost means that the operating season must be extended as long as possible to help amortize the ownership costs.

Clambunks usually build their payloads from several smaller piles over a relatively long distance during which time they must travel more-or-less straight ahead.

They require a fairly deep cutblock to use their full payload capacity. With their long loading times, clambunks are better suited for long skidding distances than for short distances. Backline distances of 400–500 m are reasonable for clambunk skidding, and distances up to 800 m are feasible, especially if the clambunk is paired with a conventional skidder. The skidder works on the front portion of the cutblock, while the clambunk works on the back end.

However, too deep a cutblock can be detrimental if the volume of timber becomes so large that it cannot all be piled easily at roadside.  One method to deal with large volume is to skid, process, and load a portion of the timber at a time. This technique requires extra travel for the processing and loading equipment, and more coordination between phases. Alternatively, the clambunk can offload the logs with its loader to pile them higher, or a secondary loader can be used.

Because the ground bearing area is larger for clambunks than for skidders, the clambunks may be able to operate on softer ground without causing excessive soil disturbance. Therefore, the operating season for clambunks can be longer than for skidders (e.g., can operate when the soil moisture content may be too high for conventional skidders).

Clambunks do very little turning compared with conventional skidders, so they are not limited by the same slope constraints. Furthermore, the weight of the load bears down on the machines which helps them from overturning. Clambunks can be operated safely on slopes up to 60%.

### ENVIRONMENTAL

Clambunks can operate on weaker soils than skidders because of their track and wheel systems (see "Tractive systems" section). Furthermore, their loading sequence requires them to travel over a portion of the skidding distance with only a partial payload. With proper planning and supervision, the partly loaded portion of the cycle could coincide with the weaker soils, thus reducing the ground impact.

Their large size and limited maneuverability make clambunks poorly suited to partial cutting operations. Their wide trails compared with conventional skidders' make it harder to protect advance regeneration.

***Forwarder*** Forwarders are highly specialized machines used in cut-to-length (CTL) systems with equipment such as feller-processors and shortwood loaders and trucks. A key feature of the CTL system is the work done by the feller-processor; it fells and delimbs the trees, cuts the stems into lengths up to 8 m long, and sorts and piles the logs for the forwarder. As the feller-processor works, it creates a debris mat from limbs and tops to distribute the weight of the machinery. After the feller-processor cuts the logs, the forwarder travels over the same debris mat to retrieve the logs. See the "Operating Techniques" section later in the handbook for additional information about the CTL system.

Forwarders are built on articulated chassis with two, three, or four axles and large rubber tires. On forwarders with two rear axles, the rear tires are usually equipped with tracks over the tires; the front axles may or may not have tracks. The rear of the forwarder consists of bunks to hold logs, and a log loader mounted behind the cab.

**Figure 16**
*A four-axle forwarder. Note that neither the front nor rear axles have tracks over the tires; such equipment is optional, although commonly used.*

**Figure 17**
*A three-axle forwarder. Note the larger tire on the single front axle.*

**Figure 18**
*A two-axle forwarder. This configuration is uncommon in British Columbia.*

The logs are loaded onto the forwarder using its log loader, and then carried to the roadside where they are unloaded.

For sorting logs, forwarders can pick individual logs from the piles created by the feller-processor to produce loads of a single type. Once a homogenous load has been moved to the roadside, it can be unloaded into its own area with little additional effort. Different sorts can also be kept separate in the machine's bunk if required.

Forwarders travel equally well forward or backward, and the operator's seat is reversible and comfortable for travelling in either direction. Depending on the layout of the particular cutblock, the forwarder may travel backward from the roadside to the felling site so that the machine is not required to turn at either end of the cycle. Forwarders can travel quite quickly over bladed trails, especially when empty. They travel more slowly over the debris mat trails, and even more slowly when loaded.

### OPERATIONAL

Economics are an important consideration in the decision to use a CTL system because they are typically more expensive *in the stump-to-truck phase* than other ground-based systems. The equipment is generally more expensive and less productive than other mechanical systems. However, the stump-to-truck costs should not be considered in isolation of benefits that may accrue to other phases. Some of these benefits include reduced soil disturbance, lengthened operating season, more stable work force, increased fibre recovery from the stand, less breakage, improved log quality, cleaner logs, better sorting, better ability to harvest short trees, and more suitability to partial cuts.

**Figure 19**
*A forwarder unloading the logs at roadside. Sawlogs and pulp logs are piled separately.*

The true worth of the CTL system can be determined only by accounting for all costs and benefits for the particular company and location. For additional information about CTL, see the discussion about "Combined Systems" in the "Operating Techniques" section later in the handbook.

Forwarders are less efficient at short skidding distances than at medium to long distances because of their comparatively long loading and unloading times. Also, short distances may provide less opportunity to make complete loads of a single sort.

Forwarders can travel up adverse pitches that could stop a conventional wheeled skidder.

Forwarders operate within fully mechanized harvesting systems in which all workers are enclosed in protective cabs; therefore, the safety hazard is low compared to non-mechanized systems. Furthermore, forwarders travel slowly compared with skidders, which further decreases the safety hazard.

**Figure 20**
*The large load raises the centre of gravity which may cause instability.*

However, the forwarder payload is carried high on the machine as compared with skidders or clambunks which raises the centre of gravity and introduces some instability. The travel routes for the forwarders should be straight down slopes to eliminate the possibility of becoming turned cross-slope and tipping over.

By travelling on a debris mat, rutting and compaction is limited to the forwarder trails. Under some conditions (e.g., soft ground or large amounts of traffic), the debris mat may become beaten into the ground, making it difficult to establish regeneration. Rehabilitating the trails may be required.

With at-the-stump processing, all the limbs and tops remain on the cutblock, which eliminates roadside accumulations and may benefit nutrient recycling on some sites.

One of the benefits of CTL systems is the ease with which the equipment can maneuver between the residual trees in a partial cutting prescription. The logs are cut short, so winding travel routes can be used to avoid damaging the residual trees. Operating successfully in a partial cut depends on the residual tree spacing and the machine size.

*Loader-forwarder* The loader-forwarder, commonly called "hoe-chucker," is a log loader used to move logs from the stump to the roadside. Most loader-forwarders are hydraulic loaders modified with high-clearance undercarriages, although line loaders can be used as loader-forwarders.

Starting from the cutblock backline, the loader-forwarder moves the logs closer to the road one step at a time by the length of its reach. The number of logs in the pile increases with each successive pass, until every log from the cutblock is piled at the roadside.

**Figure 21**
*A loader-forwarder working in a second-growth forest on Vancouver Island.*

Depending on the timber type, falling system, and processing system, the loader-forwarder may travel parallel to or perpendicular to the road. Regardless of the pattern chosen, the objective is to minimize the number of times the machine travels over each section of ground to minimize soil disturbance and operating cost.

Loader-forwarders can be outfitted with tongs for hooking logs beyond the reach of the grapple. When used with a free-spooling winch and operated by an experienced worker, the tongs can be cast up to 100 m, thus covering a substantial area. This system requires a second worker to hook the logs, and close communication between the two workers to ensure safe operations.

OPERATIONAL

The loader-forwarder is the most economical method of harvesting for gentle terrain in coastal conditions; for many operations, it has replaced the grapple yarder as the preferred harvesting system. The labour costs are low because only one worker is required.

However, loader-forwarders must handle each log several times before it reaches the roadside, so the maximum distance for moving logs is short compared with other ground-based equipment. Four or five passes with the machine is considered normal, although examples of up to 10 passes are not uncommon for special circumstances. The distance covered with each pass varies with the machine size, but for large coastal equipment, 30–35 m per pass is common, which equates to a maximum backline distance of about 150 m.

To improve their productivity, loader-forwarders are used to great advantage with other machines such as grapple yarders and skidders, especially when working around sensitive zones. The loader-forwarders can travel close to the sensitive zones, extract the logs without encroaching on the protected areas, and place the logs in a more advantageous position for the primary equipment to reach. This technique can be more economical for the overall system.

Excavators are highly mobile machines that can traverse a wide variety of terrain. The grapple can be used to stabilize the machine on steep ground to minimize the danger of overturning. Since there is only one worker with the machine, the hazard to other personnel is low.

Sideslope and soil type govern the limit to safe operation. The maximum sideslope for using a loader-forwarder is about 25–35%, especially if the sideslope is uniform. For more broken terrain, loader-forwarders can operate on steeper terrain, provided that they can travel and work safely on an acceptable route through the steep ground.

Loader-forwarders cannot work safely on thin soils overlaying bedrock because of the danger of sliding. However, the hazard can be reduced by using flotation mats. The sliding hazard is aggravated with snowfall.

### ENVIRONMENTAL

The travel routes must be planned carefully to avoid soft soils and excessively steep ground, or special precautions must be used to avoid disturbing the soil. Proper route planning is a key factor in minimizing environmental impact.

**Figure 22**
*The loader-forwarder is often the preferred machine on gentle terrain in coastal operations.*

The soil must be strong and dry enough to support the machine, although building mats with debris or using manufactured mats allows the machine to be used on softer ground. Soil disturbance is more likely to occur where the machine changes its travel direction, so turning in the more sensitive areas should be avoided. The logs harvested by a loader-forwarder are actually carried from the stump to the roadside so the logs themselves do not cause any soil disturbance.

Loader-forwarders can work in partial cutting prescriptions to remove timber without causing significant damage to the residual trees. Loader-forwarders can work safely around riparian zones without affecting the actual watercourse because these machines can reach into the stand to retrieve logs while remaining outside of the machine-free zone. Furthermore, they can move with minimal soil disturbance if the travel route avoids turns within the sensitive zone. Lastly, they can grasp standing trees that are being felled to help with directional control and avoid affecting the protected areas. These features make excavators ideally suited to working near riparian areas to harvest the timber without affecting water quality.

**Cherry picker** A cherry picker is a loader used for loading right-of-way logs directly onto log trucks without another machine having first transported the logs to the roadside. Right-of-way logs usually have the lowest production costs of all harvesting methods, and forest companies often maximize the amount of volume produced by this method.

**Figure 23**
*A coastal line loader. The boom extension ("snorkel") on this machine is quite long — identifying it as a "cherry picker" suited to working away from confined spaces such as near a yarder.*

### OPERATIONAL

Cherry pickers can be line loaders or hydraulic loaders. Line loaders can typically reach a wider area than hydraulic loaders because they can throw or "cast" the grapple beyond their normal range. The grapple can be cast 10–15 m downhill, but cannot be cast on the uphill side of the road. Extending the boom of a line loader with a "snorkel" is a common method for increasing the amount of accessible timber.

Super snorkels are specialized line loaders with boom extension up to 35 m long. The total distance from the centreline of the loader to the tip of the snorkel is about 45 m, so a significant area can be harvested without a machine actually travelling off the road surface.

The extra-long snorkel, which reduces the mobility of the machine, must be removed for transport between work sites. Super snorkels are seldom used for loading trucks because the snorkel can reach over the log truck cab, which presents an unacceptable safety hazard.

*Figure 24*
*The boom on this super snorkel has three 12-m extensions. The machine can retrieve logs about 50 m from the road without additional support equipment.*

### ENVIRONMENTAL

Since cherry pickers work directly from the road surface, their impact is limited to the road itself. Drainage structures such as ditches and culverts must remain functional during and after operations. Since super snorkels are large, heavy machines, the road and drainage structures must be built wide and firm enough to support the weight of the machine without failing.

**Horse** Horses are quiet, can maneuver easily in partial cuts, and have an aesthetic appeal to the public that gives them a special advantage in certain situations. They work well for selection and thinning operations, and near urban areas. However, they have limited productivity and can work only on gentle terrain. Furthermore, as living creatures, they require a special level of tending and handling.

### OPERATIONAL

Horses are limited to gentle terrain with favourable grades up to 25%. On steeper ground, the logs can overrun the horses. The ground must be dry or frozen, and heavy underbrush or slash can impede their travel. Snow can improve skidding conditions

**Figure 25**
*Skidding with horses in a partial cut.*

by reducing the friction between the log and the ground. All branch stubs must be trimmed so they do not poke into the ground, making the logs difficult to move. Horses can maneuver easily through partial cuts, and their low travel speed can help to minimize the scarring to residual trees.

The average skidding distance should be kept under 100 m, with long corners up to 300 m. Horses can also be used for forwarding, with the addition of a wagon or sleigh, and economic distances can be increased up to 500 m. The travel corridor must be cleared of logs or debris ahead of time because horses cannot clear their own trail.

The logs are usually piled manually at roadside in preparation for self-loading trucks.

### ENVIRONMENTAL

The main environmental advantage of horse logging, in addition to working well in thinning or selection cutting, is its quiet operation and visual appeal.

The soil disturbance caused by horses is limited to the travel corridors, but can be severe on the skid trails because the horses' ground pressure is relatively high. Soil disturbance can also be caused by the ends of the logs gouging the soil; various accessories are available to lift the logs and reduce this damage.

### Small-scale equipment

Various small winches, arches, all-terrain-vehicles (ATVs), and tractors, as well as cable systems such as chainsaw-powered winches, are available for small-scale operations. None of these systems is widely used in British Columbia. In Eastern Canada, where small woodlots constitute a higher proportion of the total harvested volume, these systems have more acceptance.

### OPERATIONAL

Small-scale equipment has low capital requirements compared with more conventional equipment. However, it is less productive, and generally limited to specialized operations.

### ENVIRONMENTAL

These systems are usually low-speed, low-impact machines that can be used in and around sensitive areas.

These machines are less likely to be used by a large company, and more likely to be used by an individual operator who may not have established management and control procedures. Environmental awareness could be lacking. On the other hand, the individual may be more aware of environmental protection. Self-discipline and environmental awareness are as important with small-scale equipment as with conventional equipment.

**Figure 26**
*A small, powered tractor which is loaded by hand. This system makes it possible for one worker to move several logs at a time.*

## Tractive system

The tractive system defines how the machine transfers the engine power to the ground to propel it forward. The four systems are rubber tires, tracks, flex tracks, and tracks over tires. These different systems affect the machine's travel speed, operating costs, stability, and soil disturbance levels.

***Rubber tires*** Rubber tires provide the highest travel speeds, although they also require the best ground conditions for travelling comfortably.

### OPERATIONAL

In general, wheeled machines are suitable for slopes up to about 35%, although steeper slopes can be crossed for short distances or by using extra care. Above 35%, machine stability decreases, traction becomes a limiting factor, and cycle times and costs increase. The high travel speed for wheeled machines

**Figure 27**
*Tire tracks are used to increase the contact area of the tire and reduce ground pressure.*

makes them suitable for longer skidding distances, especially if combined with a large payload. Typical maximum skidding distances for wheeled machines are up to 300 m, but distances up to 800 m may be feasible for machines with large payloads.

Wheeled machines are poorly suited to adverse grades. They are also adversely affected by deep snow, and may require a helper machine to build trails for travelling.

### ENVIRONMENTAL

Wheeled machines often require bladed trails for operating on slopes over 35%. Bladed trails generate siltation and occupy potential growing site. Wheeled machines typically cause more soil compaction than tracked machines. They are especially susceptible to causing damage when the soil moisture content is high.

Chains or tracked devices can be fitted to rubber tires to improve traction and reduce soil disturbance. Wide tires or dual tires increase the footprint of the machine and reduce the ground pressure, but they also make the machine more difficult to maneuver between residual stems, advance regeneration, or windfall. The operating costs are also increased with these modifications.

***Tracks*** Tracked machines are typically slower than wheeled machines, but they have increased stability, traction, and skidding power.

Tracked machines turn by varying the relative speed between the two tracks. To vary the

**Figure 28**

*A small tractor with a "high drive" track system. It provides better machine balance and elevates the drive gears above the dirt and debris.*

speed, either one track is disengaged from the drive system (i.e., with a clutch), or the distribution of power is altered between the tracks (i.e., with planetary or hydrostatic drive system). The latter method, although more complex mechanically, maintains power to both tracks at all times. Such design can result in less soil disturbance while turning.

**OPERATIONAL**

Tracked machines can typically be used on slopes up to 50%, although steeper ground can be negotiated safely for short pitches by using extreme caution. Tracked machines can skid up adverse slopes better than rubber-tired machines.

Their slower travel speed makes tracked machines more suited to shorter skidding distances, typically under 200 m. At longer distances, working with a wheeled machine is effective. The tracked machine does the initial skidding, typically from steep slopes to a staging area; the faster machine then completes the skidding to the landing.

Tracked machines do not work well on rock because of the danger of sliding, but they can work in deep snow that may stop wheeled machines from working.

The owning and operating costs for tracked undercarriages are higher than for wheeled machines.

Tracks are usually available in several widths. Narrow tracks increase the ground pressure, while wide tracks reduce the ground pressure of the machine. Wide tracks also make the machine less maneuverable, more expensive to purchase and maintain, and more prone to sliding in slippery conditions.

**ENVIRONMENTAL**

When operated appropriately, tracked machines have minimal soil impact; however, they can significantly damage soil if operated improperly. For example, operating tracked machines on sensitive soils during wet conditions can cause significant soil compaction and/or puddling.

During turning, tracked machines can cause significant soil disturbance where the machines are turned. Paying strict attention to where and how often the machines are turned can have a large impact on the soil disturbance levels.

***Flex tracks*** In contrast to conventional, rigid-frame tracked machines, flex-track machines have suspensions that allow the track to conform to the shape of the ground. This feature allows the machine to maintain ground contact over the full length of the track at all times.

On steep ground, flex-track machines are less affected than rigid-frame machines by obstacles such as stumps and windfalls. The flexible suspension allows the machines to "walk over" the obstacles by conforming to their shape and provides a higher level of stability. In contrast, conventional tracked machines have rigid track-frames that cause them to lose contact with the ground except for a short length of track when they climb over obstacles.

**Figure 29**
*The flex-track system. The wheels run on the inside of the track and are suspended independently, allowing the tracks to conform more closely to the ground profile than rigid-frame tracked machines.*

Flex-track machines can operate safely on slopes up to 60%. The tracks' ability to maintain ground contact can aid flex-track machines on adverse skids. Flex-track machines can also travel faster than conventional tracked machines, thus increasing their productivity and lowering the costs. Higher travel speed also makes them more suitable for longer skid distances.

However, these machines are generally perceived to have higher operating and maintenance costs than conventional tracked machines, and are justified for only a narrow range of sites. For example, flex-track machines may be considered for sites too steep or sensitive for conventional ground equipment, yet not steep or sensitive enough to justify cable systems.

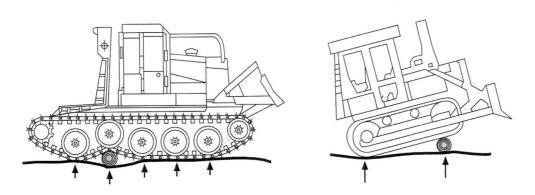

**Figure 30**
*Comparison of rigid-frame and flex-track suspensions crossing an obstacle. The weight on the rigid-frame suspension is concentrated at two points, but is spread out for the flex-track suspension. Furthermore, the rigid-frame suspension exerts a high-impact loading at the front of the track when it pivots over the obstacle.*

**ENVIRONMENTAL**

When used carefully, flex-track machines can operate on soft ground without causing rutting because they maintain full contact with the ground and cause no "pressure points" where the ground pressure is increased. The flex-track feature can further reduce soil damage because track spinning and shock loading as the machines travel over obstacles are reduced. However, these machines also travel faster than conventional tracked machines, which can lead to mechanical soil damage if they are operated carelessly on sensitive sites.

***Tires with tracks*** A common method for reducing the ground pressure and improving traction of forwarders or clambunks is to mount a set of tracks over double-bogie tires.

**Figure 31**

*Tracks increase the contact area of the wheels and decrease ground pressure. This tractive system is typical for forwarders and clambunks.*

**OPERATIONAL**

Tire-and-track machines travel quite slowly. However, they typically have large payloads that make them suitable for longer skidding distances.

**ENVIRONMENTAL**

The slow travel speed minimizes the amount of mechanical damage to the soil. The lower ground pressure compared with rubber-tired machines means that they can operate successfully on weaker soils without causing as much soil compaction. This also has the effect of extending the operating season, which can improve the operating economics.

### Method used by skidders to hold logs

Skidders can be equipped with one of three different ways of holding the logs: chokers, grapple, or swing-boom grapple. These different methods affect the suitability of the skidder to different tasks.

***Chokers*** Chokers are wire ropes for hooking the logs to the skidder. Skidders that use chokers are often called "line" or "cable" skidders.

Chokers can be pulled from the skidder for up to 25 m to hook scattered logs; the skidder does not have to travel to the logs as it would with a grapple. A single choker can be used for a single log or several logs in a bunch, and several chokers are normally used at a time.

**OPERATIONAL**

Line skidders are less expensive to purchase than grapple skidders, but their productivity is lower over short skidding distances because the hookup and unhook times are much longer. However, chokers are more suitable for long skidding distances, with scattered logs, or for situations where the skidder cannot travel right up to the log. For example, a line skidder may be used to harvest logs from a gully by stopping away from the actual hookup site and winching the logs out of the gully.

The skidder operators must climb on and off the skidder frequently to hook and unhook the chokers, which exposes them to slip-and-fall accidents, a common injury to skidder operators.

Chokers are more labour-intensive than grapples.

When skidding downhill on steep slopes, the logs may slide forward and strike the skidder. Chokers are commonly used for skidders involved in cleanup operations, such as after blowdown. Logs can be hooked and unhooked individually, which facilitates sorting.

## ENVIRONMENTAL

Chokers can be used to pull logs from riparian zones without the machine encroaching on the protected zone. For partial cutting prescriptions on sites where feller-bunchers cannot be used, chokers can retrieve the logs from among the residual trees. Chokers allow the machines to stay on designated trails, and avoid soil disturbance between the trails.

**Figure 32**
*Chokers require the operator to dismount from the machine to hook the logs.*

If the skidder encounters a section of soft ground, the winch can be disengaged, and the skidder moved ahead to better ground. The winch can be engaged, and the logs pulled into the machine. This technique, which can decrease soil disturbance, is especially valuable on adverse skids.

*Grapple* A grapple is a tong-like mechanism for grasping logs; its primary benefit is to reduce the hookup and unhook times. To hook the logs with the grapple, the skidder must drive to within a few metres of the logs and be aligned with their ends. Grapple skidders work best with feller-bunchers because making a turn with individual logs is very time-consuming.

**Figure 33**
*Hookup with a grapple is controlled from the machine's cab. This skidder uses a parallelogram mounting that allows for fore-and-aft movement of the grapple.*

## OPERATIONAL

Grapple skidders are more expensive to purchase than line skidders, but they can also be more productive. More important, however, is the requirement to use the grapple skidder with a feller-buncher. This combination increases the total capital requirements of the whole logging system and changes the business environment: switching from a line skidder to a grapple skidder requires production levels high enough to justify the capital expense of the additional equipment. Grapple skidders are better suited to high-production operations; line skidders are better suited to smaller operations.

Since the skidder must be aligned with the bunches to hook onto them, using grapple skidders can increase the amount of maneuvering, and the machine can roll over on steep slopes if the operator is not careful. On a positive note, the operator remains enclosed in a protective cab, which reduces the risk of injury.

Because grapple skidders must be immediately adjacent to the logs to hook onto them, they are poorly suited to working around sensitive riparian zones. Some grapple skidders are equipped with an auxiliary winch to use with chokers in such situations.

More maneuvering at the hookup site compared with line skidders may increase soil disturbance and increase damage to advance regeneration.

***Swing-boom grapple***   A swing-boom grapple is like a log-loader mounted on the rear of the skidder. While similar to a conventional grapple, it can reach logs farther away from the machine, especially those that lie to one side of the machine. The reach is limited to about 3 m.

**Figure 34**
*This swing-boom grapple facilitates reaching logs on either side of the skidder. Note the use of tire chains to improve traction.*

**OPERATIONAL**

Swing-boom grapples are smaller than conventional grapples, so their payload is reduced, which is a disincentive to use them exclusively.

On steep slopes, the swing-boom grapple can reach log bunches that would normally require maneuvering the machine. This feature can reduce the cycle times as well as improve the safety factor. Conversely, the weight distribution between the axles is adversely affected compared with conventional grapple skidders, which reduces the pulling ability of the skidders.

At the landing, the logs can be piled using the swing capability of the grapple without the skidder driving onto the log pile. This technique can reduce log damage.

**ENVIRONMENTAL**

The swing-boom grapple requires less turning than conventional grapples to align with the logs, which can reduce soil disturbance.

## Size

One of the most obvious distinguishing features between different machines is their size, which can make them suitable for different purposes.

**OPERATIONAL**

It is important to match the machine size to the expected timber size, turn volume, and annual production to minimize costs.

Larger machines can handle larger timber without being overloaded and with a reduced risk of mechanical failures. If insufficient timber is available to fully load a large machine, production costs will increase.

Large machines generally cost more to own and operate than small machines, both in absolute terms and hourly costs. However, they can be more productive so their unit costs can be lower. But to keep the unit costs lower, the total annual production must be higher.

This requirement makes the cost of production delays more critical for larger machines than for smaller machines; owners prefer to keep the big machines doing what they do best — harvesting timber. This preference can influence the techniques for harvesting near sensitive zones where special care may be required and production may

**Figure 35**
*A mid-size skidder with a single-action grapple mounting. This mounting has a limited range of movement compared with swing-boom grapples or parallelogram grapple mounts.*

be delayed. A strategy to reduce the effect of production delays is to use a secondary machine for special areas. This strategy allows the primary machine to continue working at full capacity, but also requires that the contractor and/or licensee be able to afford a second machine for special projects.

## ENVIRONMENTAL

Smaller machines can work better between the residual trees in a partial cutting prescription.

Large machines generally have more power than small machines, and may be better suited to working on random skid patterns on steeper ground. Where skid trails are required, large machines require larger trails to

**Figure 36**
*This conventional tractor is one of the smaller machines used for skidding. It was used in an individual-tree-selection harvesting system in second growth on Vancouver Island. A barrel used to protect the trees from scarring damage is visible on the left.*

be constructed, which can increase the amount of site disturbance. Large machines are usually better able to travel through deep snow without assistance.

## Common Features of Cable Equipment

Cable logging machines ("yarders") are positioned and anchored on the landing or truck road, and use one or more cables to drag the logs from the felling site to the landing or roadside. Cable systems require that a path be cleared in a straight line from the yarder to the backline anchor. Furthermore, the path must have a ground profile to accommodate the load path as it supports the payload.

### Cable should hang free and clear of the ground

Several factors determine the payload capacity of a cable system: the safe working tension for the cable, the anchor strength, and the cable geometry as determined by the ground profile and engineering. The distance between the chord and the cable, or "deflection," is important in determining the payload — the greater the deflection, the greater the potential payload. Since cables hang in an arc, concave ground profiles provide the maximum payload. The critical point for maximum payload can occur at any point within the span, but is usually specified as if it occurs at midspan.

*Figure 37*
*Adequate deflection and clearance are required for successful cable operations from both operational and environmental perspectives.*

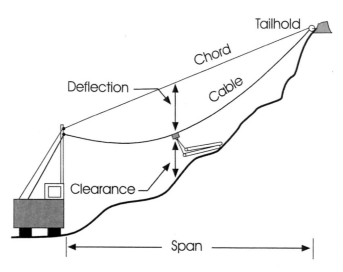

For short distances and light payloads, 6% deflection may be adequate, but for larger payloads, up to 15% deflection may be required (deflection is measured as a percentage of the horizontal span). In addition to the cable deflection, the ground profile must also provide adequate clearance for the carriage, chokers, grapple, and part of the logs' lengths as determined by the obstacle-clearance requirements. This distance can be 20 m or more below the cable for fully suspended payloads.

Adequate deflection and clearance allow for the front ends of the logs to be lifted clear of the ground as they are yarded. The term "deflection" is often used to describe the general shape of a ground profile; in this context, it refers to the combination of deflection and clearance. While not strictly correct, it provides a good measure for the suitability of the profile for successful cable operations. Ultimately, the user must include clearance in the analysis.

When used with the appropriate yarding system, backspars, intermediate supports, or both can increase ground clearance in areas of insufficient deflection.

*Figure 38*
*A mid-sized swing yarder capable of grapple or skyline yarding. Its small size allows for easy transport between work sites.*

Inadequate deflection and clearance may limit the maximum yarding distance to less than the machine's capacity. Payload will be reduced below optimal, reducing productivity and increasing costs. Without adequate clearance, the cables could drag on the ground and the logs may cause soil disturbance or become stuck behind obstacles. Proper engineering before falling commences ensures that deflection and clearance will be adequate to harvest the timber from all parts of the cutblock.

Productivity is reduced when logs become stuck or equipment is broken because of poor deflection. The risk of debris being tossed through the air and striking a worker or of cables breaking and causing injury increases with poor deflection.

Too much deflection can increase cycle times for skylines because of the increased time required to lower the chokers from the carriage to the ground and then back to the carriage.

### ENVIRONMENTAL

Ground disturbance usually occurs in areas of poor deflection where the leading end of the log cannot be lifted clear of the ground. Full and partial suspension are discussed in more detail in the "Operating Techniques" section of this handbook.

The cable must lie in a straight line from the yarder to the tailhold. Therefore, a straight corridor must be cut through the residual trees when a cable system is used for a partial cutting prescription.

**Figure 39**
*A skyline corridor cut through a second-growth stand on Vancouver Island. The corridor is approximately 4 m wide, and cut in a straight line from the yarder to the backspar. It allows the skyline cable to hang free and clear, without any interference from the ground or the residual trees.*

## Traffic over the ground is reduced

Machine traffic on the ground is virtually eliminated with cable systems compared with ground-based systems (mobile backspars are sometimes used). Logs can be lifted clear of the ground with some cable systems, although partial suspension is more common. A significant amount of soil disturbance can occur near the landing, where the logs usually touch the ground.

The ground disturbance caused by the logs can become a pathway for surface water to travel and cause erosion. See the "Machine mobility" section for a discussion of the differences between towers, swing yarders, and yarding direction relating to surface-water flow.

### OPERATIONAL

The labour and equipment requirements for cable yarding often make it more expensive to own and operate than ground-based systems. Depending on the capability of the specific yarder, road construction costs can be reduced by increasing the yarding distances.

The machinery does not usually leave the truck road, which reduces the risk of soil damage and its subsequent effect on water quality. With the proper setup, deflection, and operation, trees can be lifted out of gullies or over streams without operating any equipment near the stream channel.

Logs can be lifted over existing plantations or other sensitive zones without having to construct roads or skid trails through the protected zones. However, full suspension does not necessarily ensure zero impact — debris may fall from the logs or the logs may knock into saplings as they swing from side to side.

Backspar trails may be required for grapple yarding; their locations must be planned carefully to minimize site disturbance.

### The yarder and cable are anchored when operating

The yarder is anchored to the ground at one end of the span and one or more tailholds are anchored at the other end.

**Figure 40**
*A highlead tower operating from a landing. Three guylines hold the tower in position.*

The anchors must be strong enough to support the tower, cable, and payload. Stumps are typically used for anchors, but in some situations, stumps are either unavailable or inadequate. In these situations, fabricated anchors such as rock bolts or "deadmen" will be required. With grapple yarders, auxiliary machines such as excavators or crawler tractors are often used as mobile backspars.

OPERATIONAL

Anchoring the tower at each setup requires a certain amount of time, the cost of which must be amortized over the volume to be harvested from that setup. Furthermore, the tailhold must be moved continually from one location to another during yarding to cover the cutblock. In this respect, cable yarding is different from either ground-based or aerial systems because a higher proportion of the total time is spent in setup activities for which there is no production. The costs for this non-productive time must be amortized over the volume harvested at setup, making the cost for cable yarding particularly sensitive to the volume of timber per unit area. In partial cuts, less timber is removed and more setups are required, thus increasing the harvesting costs.

Some cable machines are designed for ease of mobility, with minimal setup and moving time, while others require a significant amount of setup time. For example, a long-distance skyline yarder may require several days for each setup, while a small, mobile yarder may be ready for operations within a few hours of arriving at the work site.

Pulling a guyline anchor or tailhold out of the ground can result in the tower falling over or the main cables being whipped around the work site. Either situation is very dangerous, and all anchors must be checked thoroughly to ensure that they are safe.

The stumps remaining in a plantation may be too decayed to use as anchors. If fabricated anchors are required, holes may be excavated to bury "deadman" anchors, which could destroy some existing regeneration. Alternatively, a machine such as an excavator or tractor may be parked in the plantation to use as an anchor.

## Roads required within yarding distance

The maximum yarding distance with cable systems is limited by the amount of cable carried by the yarder, and can be reduced to less than the maximum capacity by inadequate deflection and clearance. A typical maximum yarding distance is between 200 and 400 m, although some specialized machines can reach up to 2000 m or more.

### OPERATIONAL

Careful engineering and layout is required to ensure that all the timber lies within yarding distance. In contrast to ground-based or aerial systems that incur only incremental costs to travel additional distance, timber beyond the reach of the cables is difficult to retrieve. Cable extensions can sometimes be added, or additional road may be required, both of which are expensive solutions.

Different cable logging systems have different economical yarding distances, depending on cable speeds and payload. Swing yarders configured for grapple yarding typically retrieve logs one at a time, and are short-distance machines (under 200 m). Configured as skylines, they can operate up to 400 m. Long-distance skyline yarders can operate successfully over distances of 1000 m or more, while highlead machines typically operate in the 200–300 m range.

### ENVIRONMENTAL

Longer yarding distances can reduce the road network density, which can reduce the amount of siltation generated from the roads and reduce the amount of productive land occupied by roads.

## Uphill or downhill yarding is feasible

Cable systems can be used for both uphill and downhill yarding, although they often work better uphill.

### OPERATIONAL

The cables remain in tension at all times with uphill yarding and the logs are always under the operator's control. With downhill yarding, the logs tend to slide ahead and may be uncontrolled. On steep downhill yarding, the logs may slip out of the choker and slide down to the road, perhaps striking the machinery or workers. Proper placement of the yarder on the landing or road is critical to ensure safe working conditions.

Log breakage may be reduced in uphill yarding because the logs are always fully controlled. In downhill yarding, the operator has less control of the logs, and breakage is more likely. With uphill yarding, the logs tend to slide over the stumps more easily because of the shape of the stumps and the upward pull of the cable, so hangups and delays are reduced compared with downhill.

Swing yarders configured for grapple yarding are an exception — they are better suited for downhill yarding because the logs are easier to land and pile in this direction. Also, the operator has improved visibility.

Surface water flows down the depressions left by dragging the logs over the ground. With downhill yarding, especially with tower yarding, the tracks tend to converge, thus the runoff tends to converge. With uphill yarding, the tracks tend to diverge, thus spreading out the runoff. See the "Machine mobility" section for a discussion of the differences between tower and swing yarders, and how the yarding direction can influence the erosion caused by water flowing in the yarding tracks.

**Figure 41**
*Moving cables always represent a safety hazard. To avoid accidents when working with cable systems, workers must remain alert and aware of their surroundings at all times.*

### Moving cables pose a safety hazard
There is an inherent safety hazard of working near moving cables.

Workers must be aware of the increased hazards posed by moving cables compared with ground-based systems. The increased hazard also results in a higher classification rating and increased fees for workers' insurance coverage. The fire hazard posed by cable friction during hot weather requires the use of an after-work watchman once the fire hazard rating has reached specified levels.

## Distinguishing Features of Cable Equipment

The various yarders can be distinguished from one another by four major features: configuration, degree of mobility, method used to hold the logs, and machine size.

**Figure 42**
*A highlead yarder.*

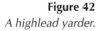
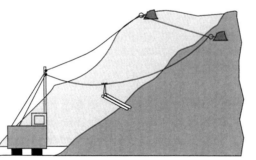

### Highlead and skyline configurations
All cable systems share one characteristic: a cable fastened to a drum on a winch is used to pull a payload from one location to another. Beyond that, a wide variety of configurations and complexities is possible, although two basic ways to lift the payload off the ground describe the main differences: highlead and skyline.

**Figure 43**
*A running skyline.*

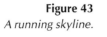
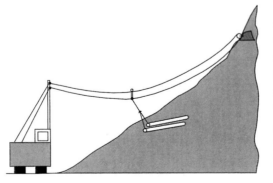

A highlead system consists of only two cables, and operates much like a clothesline. By comparison, a skyline system uses a carriage running on a cable to lift the logs fully or partially off the ground and transport them to roadside. Skylines have many variations, but the addition of a carriage distinguishes skyline systems from highlead systems.

Single-span skylines can be rigged with backspars to elevate the tailhold, and improve deflection. If the deflection is inadequate, then one or more intermediate supports must be added, thus defining the multi-span skyline.

Some yarders can be configured as different cable systems by using different set-ups, cables, and carriages.

*Highlead*  The simplest cable system consists of a yarder with a two-drum winch, one of which holds a heavy cable called the mainline, while the other holds a lighter cable called the haulback. The haulback is fastened to the mainline at the point where the chokers are attached using an apparatus called "butt-rigging." From the butt-rigging, the haulback is run through two sheaves anchored at the backline and back to the yarder. The butt-rigging is raised by applying tension to one line and braking pressure to the other. Typically, only one end of the logs is lifted from the ground.

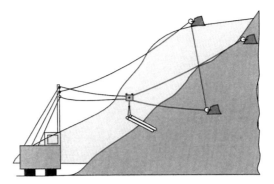

**Figure 44**
*A live skyline with motorized slackpulling carriage.*

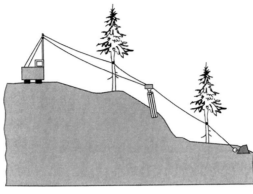

**Figure 45**
*A multi-span skyline.*

### OPERATIONAL

Highlead is considered the most rudimentary cable system because its equipment requirements are minimal. Any two-drum yarder can be rigged for highlead yarding. Capital costs and training requirements are lowest of any of the cable systems.

Highlead yarding is relatively unsophisticated. It can be used when deflection is poor because the system will still work even if the cables contact the ground. This practice can cause excessive soil disturbance and reduced productivity, and should be avoided if possible.

By attaching a block that runs on the haulback to the butt-rigging, the highlead system can be converted into a running skyline system to provide additional lifting capacity.

**Figure 46**
*A highlead yarder typical of coastal cable systems. Chokers are attached to the butt-rigging, visible about halfway up the tower.*

### ENVIRONMENTAL

It is difficult to lift the payload completely off the ground because the lift is provided via braking pressure: the only way to lift the payload is to increase the braking pressure on the haulback. This means that one end of the logs must always drag across the ground.

*Skyline*  A wide variety of skyline systems is available, from simple conversions of highlead systems, to purpose-built highly mobile swing yarders, to large skyline

towers. Furthermore, skylines can be rigged in many different ways, depending on the equipment, the workers' skill and experience, and the requirements of the site. The common characteristic of all these systems is that a cable provides lift to a carriage by means other than simple braking pressure on the haulback.

The carriage must run clear of the ground at all locations along the skyline. The carriage can run on the haulback cable (as in grapple yarders), in which case it is called a running skyline, or it can run on a separate cable. If the skyline can be raised and lowered during yarding, it is called a live skyline or slackline; a skyline that is fixed in position during yarding is known as a standing skyline.

Skylines are built in a wide range of sizes, as discussed later in this section.

### OPERATIONAL

The main benefit of skylines is that the logs can be given more lift, thus reducing hangups, providing clearance over sensitive zones, extending the yarding distance, and reducing soil disturbance (assuming that the ground profile provides adequate deflection and clearance). Logs can be either fully or partially suspended, as discussed in the "Operating Techniques" section.

Skyline systems require more highly trained workers than highlead systems, especially if backspars are required. The availability of trained workers may be a concern. The

cables carry higher loads than highlead systems, so the workers must be more aware of the hazards of working with cables. More safety items must be checked, and communication between various workers becomes more critical. More planning and engineering are also required.

The capital costs are higher because of the more sophisticated machinery and the extra hardware required. Setup costs may be increased because of the system complexity. For very large cutblocks, helicopters may be required to transport crew and equipment from the road to the work sites.

### ENVIRONMENTAL

Skylines provide capabilities that are unavailable in less sophisticated cable systems. They can be used to carry logs over sensitive zones or plantations with minimal impact. Some skylines can extend over 2000 m to provide access to areas without roads.

Depending on cutblock size, a large volume of timber can flow through skyline landings, which can result in site disturbance around the landing.

Skyline systems, with their ability to use slackpulling carriages, can work in partial cutting prescriptions where highlead systems cannot operate. However, not all skyline systems are equally well suited to partial cutting. Cable movement within the corridor, with its potential for damaging residual trees, should be considered for assessing the system's suitability; running skylines have the most cable movement. Residual trees can also be damaged as the logs are pulled into the skyline corridor.

***Multi-span skyline***   Multi-span skylines use intermediate supports to circumvent the problem of inadequate deflection on uniform or convex slopes. A "jack" is suspended from a tree in one or more locations to hold the skyline off the ground, and a special carriage that can pass over the jack is required.

OPERATIONAL

Suitable equipment must be used to make multi-span skylines feasible. The yarder must be configured correctly, and the carriage must be capable of passing over a jack. Rigging a multi-span skyline adds more complexity to the system compared with other cable systems, and requires more worker training. The number of workers skilled in multi-span yarding limits the use of these skylines.

**Figure 49**
*This intermediate support was suspended on a cable between two trees. The carriage is about to pass over the support.*

Companies disagree on the usefulness of multi-span skylines. FERIC found during the interviews that multi-span skylines should either be "used wherever possible" or "avoided at all costs," depending on corporate experience. Productivity was reported as either better or worse than conventional cable systems. Notwithstanding the differing opinions on their suitability and cost-effectiveness, multi-span skylines can be used to reach areas of poor deflection without the need of additional roads.

ENVIRONMENTAL

Soil disturbance can occur in areas of poor deflection, and multi-span skylines are one method of harvesting these areas with less soil disturbance. Any skyline allows for roads to be located away from sensitive areas — multi-span skylines extend this capability into areas where single-span skylines might not reach without additional road construction. Multi-span skylines are well suited to partial cutting prescriptions because the intermediate supports keep the skyline within the corridor.

## Yarder mobility

Although yarders remain more-or-less stationary while working, they can be divided into two classes based on their degree of mobility. Towers are intended for use in one place for an extended period of time, while swing yarders are designed to move relatively quickly between sites.

***Tower***   Towers are vertical spar trees that are anchored to fixed locations while yarding. The cutblock is harvested by moving the tailhold from one location to another between

**Figure 50**
*Towers are anchored in one location when operating. They require substantial landings to provide space for the logs, loader, and truck. This tower was rigged for skyline yarding using a slackpulling carriage.*

yarding "roads." The tower itself is not moved between roads, resulting in an overall fan-shaped pattern.

### OPERATIONAL

Since all the logs are yarded to a single location, landings can become congested. After unhooking and piling a number of logs, the pile can become too high for safe working conditions. The landing must provide sufficient room for the machines to be positioned with safe clearances all around for the on-the-ground workers, and for landing, processing, storing, and loading the logs. Much activity is concentrated in a small area, and safety can be a concern, especially on steep, difficult ground where landing size is usually restricted.

An auxiliary machine should work with the yarder to keep the landing clear of logs. In coastal operations, a loader usually works with the yarder, while in the Interior, a skidder is often used to forward the logs to another landing. In either case, costs are higher because the productivity of the second machine is governed by the yarder productivity even though it can produce more.

Two techniques to help manage the costs of the auxiliary machine are to operate two towers close together, servicing both with a single loader, or to use the loader for primary transport ("cherry-picking") during its idle times. The ability to work in simultaneously from two landings depends highly on good planning and the site and terrain conditions.

In small cutblocks all the timber can possibly be piled in one spot and an auxiliary machine may not be required.

**Figure 51**
*Lacking the ability to swing, towers must drop the logs in a pile beside the landing.*

The crew size for tower yarders is typically larger than for swing yarders, because chokers are used almost exclusively, and moving the tower and tailhold is a laborious process. Crews of five to seven workers are typical for large highlead towers, although low-production systems require as few as two workers.

### ENVIRONMENTAL

Towers are typically taller than swing yarders, so they have improved deflection for any given location, which can result in less soil disturbance over the entire cutblock. However, the tracks left by dragging the logs over the ground are concentrated around the landing which can cause high levels of soil disturbance in specific areas.

For uphill yarding, any surface drainage flowing in the tracks left by the logs will be dispersed; however, the reverse is true for downhill yarding, and the water will be concentrated at the landing. This can cause soil erosion if the water is left uncontrolled at the landing. Proper control involves adequate ditching and regular maintenance.

Landings located near gullies can cause problems. On one hand, material must not enter the gully because of water quality and slope stability concerns. On the other hand, a landing location near the gully can improve deflection and provide lift to the logs. Alternative landing locations and harvesting systems must be examined thoroughly before proposing a landing that encroaches on a gully.

The space occupied by landings may be a concern because it reduces the available growing site.

The inability to swing may be a concern in partial cutting — the logs remain piled inside the corridor after they are unhooked unless an auxiliary machine is used. Parallel corridors oriented perpendicular to the contours are preferred, but some fan-shaped corridors may be needed if the terrain dictates (e.g., when the yarder is positioned on a nose or ridge).

*Swing yarder*  Swing yarders are distinguished from towers by their basic construction: they have rotating superstructures and inclined booms and are built on track-mounted or rubber-tired carriers. Swing yarders, which face the harvesting site when yarding but can swing to either side to pile the logs, can thus work from an ordinary road surface as well as from a landing. In addition, swing yarders typically have only two guylines. This feature, combined with their basic construction, allows swing yarders to be moved more easily than towers.

Historically in British Columbia, swing yarders have been rigged with grapples rather than chokers, although most can be rigged with either system as required. Rigging them as grapple yarders limits them to short-distance yarding.

**Figure 52**
*Swing yarders can be used in roadside applications, without the need of a landing. This large swing yarder, rigged with a slackpulling carriage, will land the logs on the road surface.*

OPERATIONAL

The ability to pile logs away from the immediate landing area allows swing yarders to work independently of a loader, which reduces costs. The crew size is usually smaller than for towers, which also reduces costs. Swing yarders are easier and less costly than towers to move between setups. When configured for grapple yarding, safety improves, and when equipped with lights, grapple yarders can be used for nighttime operations. The relative preference between swing yarders and towers is different between the Coast and the Interior — swing yarders are generally preferred on the Coast, whereas towers are preferred in the Interior. The reasons are related to ownership costs, productivity, and timber size. For any given size class, swing yarders are more expensive to purchase than towers, and the owner must consider the ratio between ownership costs and productivity. Since productivity is often related to payload size, and payloads can be kept high when using a grapple in coastal stands because of larger trees, the higher ownership costs can be offset by higher productivity. However, grapples are impractical for many interior locations because of the small average tree size and a corresponding small pay-load size. Therefore, the higher ownership costs are not offset by a corresponding increase in productivity, and towers are preferred for their lower ownership costs. This relationship can be altered by bunching the trees, which essentially increases the pay-load even with a small average tree size.

### ENVIRONMENTAL

Landings may or may not be required. Roadside logging may result in more plugged ditches and culverts; the drainage must be re-established after logging.

The yarding roads for swing yarders are generally parallel to one another. This pattern tends to avoid concentrating any surface water flow into a single location, and thus avoids the detrimental effects of accumulated water that happen with towers.

Swing yarders are well suited for partial cutting because they can pull the logs completely out of the corridor for piling on the road, where they are easily accessible. Moving between corridors is easy because of the few guylines required to anchor the yarder.

Swing yarders configured for grapple yarding are limited to short yarding distances, and require that haul roads be located close together. Swing yarders equipped with slackpulling carriages can yard over longer distances, with a corresponding increase in road spacing.

***Sled*** The original yarders in British Columbia used wooden spar trees with sled-mounted winches. The sled was dragged between sites—a time-consuming process. Sleds have been replaced almost entirely by self-propelled, mobile carriers; however, some specialized yarders still use sleds for carriers.

**Figure 53**

*The European cable crane system uses a sled-mounted yarder with a single drum. The carriage runs on a fixed skyline. During yarding, the logs are lowered from the felling site to the haul road at the bottom of the hill.*

### OPERATIONAL

Sleds can be moved between locations with no road access. For example, European cable cranes are usually used for long-span skylines and require the winch to be located at the top of the hill, or another area devoid of roads. These yarders can be transported by helicopter after disassembly, or can move under their own power by pulling on a stump in the desired direction of travel. Once in position, the sled is anchored to trees or stumps.

### ENVIRONMENTAL

Some roads may be unnecessary to build with the European cable crane system. Fewer roads can mean fewer sources for generating sediment, less potential for mass wasting, and less land removed from the productive land base. The

**Figure 54**

*This sled-mounted yarder for a European cable crane is anchored to trees at the top of the corridor. The large fan on the right-hand side of the sled acts as an air brake to control the carriage's speed as it descends on the skyline.*

reduction in the road network is especially important considering the typical location of the roads made redundant by this yarding system — steep, rough, and unstable terrain often associated with difficult road construction.

## Method used to hold logs

Two basic ways are used to hold the logs for cable systems: chokers and grapples. The same issues for chokers versus grapples (e.g., hookup and unhook time, accessibility to logs) apply to cable systems as to ground-based systems and are discussed previously.

*Chokers* Chokers are wire ropes for hooking the logs to the butt-rigging or carriage. Chokers allow for several logs to be yarded in each turn — either with several chokers used at a time, or one choker holding several logs.

OPERATIONAL

Multi-span skylines and yarders with slackpulling carriages must be used with chokers. Towers use chokers almost exclusively.

The workers must be well clear of the hookup site before the turn is pulled into the landing. They must also be far enough away that any debris that is dislodged dur-

ing yarding cannot reach them. On steep or rugged ground, the time involved for moving to safety can be significant.

Most chokers must be unhooked manually once the logs reach the landing, a task usually performed by a worker other than the yarder operator. Effective communications between the two workers is essential to maintain a safe working environment. For smaller yarders designed for one-person operations, the cab is located near the ground so the operator can unhook the chokers without a second worker. Alternatively, various models of self-releasing chokers have been developed that allow the yarder operator to release the chokers remotely without requiring a second worker. Such chokers can improve the safe working environment and reduce costs.

When grapple yarding, chokers can be used to reach areas of poor deflection. They are useful during cleanup to reach isolated logs.

ENVIRONMENTAL

Chokers are often used on difficult ground where a grapple cannot be used because of poor deflection, and soil disturbance may result. While the chokers do not *cause* soil disturbance, they may be associated with the soil disturbance in these poor-deflection areas.

**Figure 55**
*Chokers can be attached directly to the carriage, as with this gravity slackline yarding system. This attachment method limits the lateral yarding capability to within the length of the chokers, thus requiring more frequent changes of the tailhold anchor.*

**Figure 56**
*Several logs can be hooked at once when using chokers. The chokers on this slackpulling carriage are attached to a dropline, thus allowing for a wide swath to be covered.*

***Grapples*** Grapples are tongs used to hold the logs. Unlike grapples on ground-based equipment, gravity and cable tension control the opening and closing action, respectively.

OPERATIONAL

The hookup and unhook times are greatly reduced with grapples, which can improve productivity, but the effect on productivity also depends on turn volumes. Grapples typically hold just one log at a time, so the average turn volume may be quite small if

the tree size is small. On some sites, it may be feasible to use a feller-buncher for falling or a loader-forwarder to pre-bunch the trees to increase the average payload size.

A high skill level is required to balance the tensions in all the cables to operate the grapple efficiently, and the difficulty increases with yarding distance. Hookup is easiest if the operator can see the logs, which further limits the maximum yarding distance. At longer distances, the operator may require a spotter with a radio to help with hooking the logs. Operations become difficult during inclement weather because of reduced visibility.

For these reasons, grapples are not well suited to long yarding distances (over 200 m).

Safety improves when using grapples. The crew size is smaller, and the hazard exposure for the remaining workers is reduced because they can stay farther away from the moving cables. Using mobile backspars reduces the amount of manual labour for road changes and ensures that all workers are enclosed in protective cabs when the lines are being moved.

Unlike chokers, the grapple can hook onto logs that may be partially buried in the soil or covered by snow. Grapples may cause more log breakage than chokers, especially for small trees that can be broken easily. Recovery of broken slabs may be more effective with grapples (Forrester 1995).

ENVIRONMENTAL

The road density is greater with grapples compared with chokers because of the shorter yarding distance. Grapple yarders are often used with mobile backspars, which may require trails to be constructed, so the amount of land susceptible to soil disturbance is increased.

## Size
The range of sizes for yarders is wider than for any other equipment class. The smallest yarders are about 8 m high, are mounted on trailers, and can be pulled easily by small vehicles, while large skyline towers stand over 30 m high and weigh over 100 tonnes.

OPERATIONAL

In general, the machine size determines the amount of cable that can be carried, the ability to yard over difficult terrain (taller means more deflection), pulling power, mobility, and crew size requirements. Large machines are expensive, and are better

**Figure 58 (L)**
*Large towers require six to eight guylines to hold them in position. The tower is raised part way using a large hydraulic ram, and then pulled upright with the guylines.*

**Figure 59 (R)**
*A mid-sized tower that can be equipped for highlead or skyline operations.*

suited to high-production operations in large cutblocks where the setup time can be amortized over a larger volume. Smaller yarders are more economical than large yarders on smaller cutblocks because their setup time is less, and can be amortized economically over a smaller volume.

The machine must be matched in size to move the largest logs. In stands with a wide range of tree sizes, a machine large enough to handle the largest logs may be uneconomic for the smaller timber. With more uniform trees, such as in coastal second-growth stands or in the Interior, the machine size can be matched more closely to the average tree size. Using a feller-buncher on smaller timber to increase the average payload volume can help improve the yarding economics.

Large yarders require more substantial guyline anchors than the smaller machines, and more substantial tailholds when used for long-span skylines. If the cutblock is adjacent to a plantation, the stumps may be too badly decayed to serve as anchors, so fabricated anchors will be required. This step may involve burying "deadman" anchors or using rock bolts. Either option requires additional equipment.

**Figure 60**
*Small yarders are mounted on skidders for improved mobility.*

Machine size drastically affects the ease of mobility for the yarder, especially if travel on public roads is required between cutblocks. Some yarders are specially designed to the maximum size allowable for travel on public roads without dismantling. Even on private roads, the yarder size may be a factor in road design. Large swing yarders configured for grapple yarding require wide roads for safe working and tall skyline yarders may have difficulty negotiating tight switchbacks on narrow roads.

The size versus capacity relationship has exceptions. For example, yarders for the European cable crane system are relatively small machines that are designed specially for long-distance yarding up to 1200 m or more. See the "Machine mobility" section for more detail.

### ENVIRONMENTAL

Large machines can generally carry more cable and yard over longer distances than small machines. More height can also help with areas of poor deflection, although large cable capacity and good engineering that take full advantage of the ground profile are also important. Longer yarding distances result in a less dense road network.

Large yarders can fully suspend the payload over sensitive sites. Small yarders are also capable of full suspension, but usually over shorter yarding distances.

## Number of drums on the yarder

Each cable requires a separate drum, and a yarder can have up to four drums. In addition to drums for the operating lines, yarders usually have a strawline drum for the workers to pull the other cables into position.

### OPERATIONAL

In general, the number of drums determines the skyline configurations that can be used with the yarder. With one drum, the yarder is limited to systems like the European cable crane. A two-drum yarder can be used for highlead or simple skylines like the shotgun system. For slackpulling with a two-drum winch, a carriage that can clamp to the skyline is required; adding more lines removes the clamping requirement. For example, adding a third drum allows for slackpulling with a motorized carriage and a live skyline, or with a non-motorized carriage and a running skyline. Adding a fourth drum allows for slackpulling with a live skyline with a non-motorized carriage. Grapple yarding is a special case of a three-drum yarder and a running skyline.

Specialized yarders and carriages can achieve some of these capabilities with fewer drums. Additional drums increase the complexity and capital cost of the yarder, and the skill-level requirement for workers.

## Interlocked winch

Some yarders are equipped with interlocked winches, in which the mainline and haulback drums are linked mechanically or hydraulically. The interlock captures the power from one drum and returns it to the other drum instead of wasting it in the form of heat as happens with non-interlocked winches that use brakes to maintain tension. As one drum turns to wind in the cable, the other drum automatically pays out an equal amount of cable.

### OPERATIONAL

Since braking pressure is not used to hold the lines in tension, less energy is consumed during yarding. Higher line speeds are also possible, thus allowing for longer yarding distances to be economical. Interlocked winches provide more control over the turn as it is being yarded, so that log breakage is reduced. In grapple yarders, the interlocks also offer more control over the grapple as the logs are being hooked — productivity can be increased because of the extra control.

Interlocked yarders may be used in areas with less deflection than conventional yarders. Higher line tensions are required to hold the same payload, and the loading on tailholds is increased. Line wear also increases and more care must be taken to ensure that the tailhold anchors can withstand the yarding forces.

### ENVIRONMENTAL

The better control over the line tensions allows grapple yarders equipped with interlocked winches to work more effectively than non-interlocked machines in gullied terrain. This feature provides the possibility of moving the machine to a different location that may be preferable from an environmental perspective.

## Slackpulling carriage

The lateral yarding capability of highlead yarders is limited to the length of the chokers. Skyline yarders can use slackpulling carriages with lateral yarding capability to extend the reach. The cable to which the chokers are attached is called the dropline, tongline, or skidding line. The chokers can be pulled 30 m or more from the skyline road using a dropline.

Slackpulling carriages can be divided into manual or mechanical types, and the mechanical carriages can be further subdivided into those where the line is pulled by the yarder and those where it is pulled by the carriage (Studier 1993).

### OPERATIONAL

A slackpulling carriage makes a wider band of timber available to each yarding road, which helps to amortize the setup costs at a lower rate.

**Figure 61**
*This slackpulling carriage is a simple modification of a grapple carriage. The grapple was removed, and the closing-line used as the dropline.*

Fewer setups are required to cover the entire cutblock when a slackpulling carriage is used.

Two sets of chokers can be used with a slackpulling carriage, and the workers can be hooking one set while the second set is being yarded to the landing with a payload. Preset or "hot and cold" chokers can improve productivity significantly. This technique requires close coordination between the yarder operator and the hookup crew to ensure safe operations.

The skyline carriage must be designed specifically to accommodate a dropline. The types available range in complexity from simple modifications of grapple-yarder carriages to self-clamping carriages to radio-controlled, motorized carriages with separate drums for the dropline. The owning and operating costs vary according to the complexity of the carriage.

### ENVIRONMENTAL

A slackpulling carriage makes partial cutting feasible; without the slackpulling capability, the chokers could not reach beyond the skyline corridor, and cable harvesting would be impractical.

## Common Features of Aerial Systems

Aerial systems include both helicopters and balloons. Helicopters lift the logs directly from the felling site to a truck road or water drop, while balloon systems are essentially two-drum systems with a lighter-than-air balloon tethered to the butt-rigging to lift the payload into the air. Since balloons have been used only sporadically in the logging industry, this discussion will focus on helicopters.

### Roads can be far from the cutting site

Aerial logging systems are unique in that they can fly the timber from one location to another without regard to intervening obstacles. With helicopters, economics determines the maximum flying distance, but with balloon systems, the yarder's cable capacity determines the maximum yarding distance.

In some remote coastal areas, helicopters are used without roads at all — the logs are dropped directly into the ocean or lake.

**Figure 62**
*Helicopters can reach remote areas without the need to construct roads. The cutblocks on this ridge were logged with helicopters.*

**OPERATIONAL**

Costly roads across unstable terrain can be eliminated, and high-value timber in remote locations can be harvested.

The economic flying distance for helicopters, which depends upon the timber values and the helicopter payload capacity, may be over 2 km.

The vertical relationship between the felling site and the landing can influence the economics. The road should be located below the felling site, although it is feasible to lift logs to a higher landing. The flight angle to the landing must not be too steep for the selected model of helicopter.

**ENVIRONMENTAL**

Eliminating road construction across unstable terrain will reduce the road network and its associated erosion. Difficult stream crossings may be eliminated. Trees can be harvested from inaccessible locations to salvage trees damaged by fire, disease, or insects.

Any post-harvesting surveys and treatments must be planned and accounted for during the harvesting activities because the areas will be roadless, and access may be difficult and costly.

### Logs are lifted clear of the ground and obstacles

Once the logs have been hooked and lifted, they do not touch the ground until they are deposited on the landing.

**OPERATIONAL**

Workers must be made aware of the hazards associated with overhead equipment, especially in partial cutting prescriptions.

On-block skid roads and the associated soil disturbance are eliminated. Logs can be transported over existing plantations or other sensitive areas without causing damage.

Helicopters can be used in clearcuts, or they can be used to lift individual trees through the residual canopy in a partial cutting prescription.

## Equipment is expensive

Helicopters are more expensive to own and operate than other harvesting equipment.

### OPERATIONAL

In addition to the aircraft itself, helicopter harvesting requires an extensive support crew and equipment that is not typically available to the average logger. Helicopter operations are labour-intensive, and the high cost of operations can be recovered only by maximizing productivity and log value.

Specialized crews for specific cutblocks are typical. Mobilization costs are high, and must be amortized over the cutblock volume. A substantial volume of timber for harvesting must be scheduled to keep the per-unit mobilization costs within acceptable limits.

## Equipment capacity must closely match resource

The yarding capacity of the helicopter is strictly limited by its lifting capacity.

### OPERATIONAL

The payload must not exceed the lifting capacity of the helicopter. If the tree size exceeds the lifting capacity of the helicopter, then the trees must be cut into shorter lengths. Logs may be manufactured according to their weight, rather than by the most desirable length.

The ability to drop part of the load under pilot control is an important feature — a two-part hook with independent control on both parts provides this ability. The ground crew hooks up the logs according to their estimated weight, but the pilot makes the final decision about which logs to fly. Little time is wasted dropping the excess weight.

**Figure 63**
*A helicopter lifting tree-length logs near Boston Bar. Matching the helicopter size to the tree size allowed for full-tree logging.*

Similarly, underloading the helicopter wastes its capacity and is expensive. Ground crews must be trained thoroughly to ensure that the helicopter is loaded to its optimum payload.

## Landing is busy

Helicopter operations typically have several hookup crews in different locations to ensure that the helicopter is not delayed during hookup. Usually only one landing is active at a time, resulting in a work site that can become congested.

**Figure 64**

*The workers on this landing must be constantly aware of the helicopter's position and remain in the clear as it approaches the landing.*

OPERATIONAL

Helicopters are expensive to operate, and any delays can be very costly. Activities must be well coordinated to ensure that costs are acceptable and that all workers in the landing can operate in a safe environment.

## Weather and climate affect operations

As flying machines, helicopters are more seriously affected by adverse weather than other types of logging equipment.

OPERATIONAL

Operations must be shut down during adverse weather such as fog and high wind. Hot weather or high altitude can affect the lifting capacity of the helicopters and reduces their payload. The climate in the operating area should be considered to ensure a reasonable number of flying days during the proposed operating period.

## Distinguishing Features of Aerial Systems

### Size

Helicopter models commonly used for logging in British Columbia range in lifting capacity from 1600 to about 12 000 kg. The size also determines the owning and operating costs, which can run into thousands of dollars per hour.

OPERATIONAL

For all helicopter sizes, the high cost and productivity place a high premium on proper planning — the entire operation must be well coordinated to minimize delays. Fallers, choker setters, flight crews, landing personnel, and maintenance personnel must all be well trained for maximum efficiency. This training becomes even more important with larger helicopters because of their extremely high operating costs.

**Figure 65**

*This helicopter is purpose-built for external lifting. It has two counter-rotating rotors and no tail rotor, and seats only one person.*

The decision where to buck the trees into logs is critical to helicopter operations because of lifting limitations. If the timber is large and the helicopter is small, then short logs must be manufactured at the stump, possibly reducing log value. Larger helicopters can help maximize log value because of their larger payloads — longer logs can be manufactured and lifted. As the timber size decreases, the number of options increases — with smaller timber, the trees may not even require bucking, and smaller helicopters may still be able to lift the trees intact.

**Figure 66**
*Small helicopters are used for support services such as ferrying workers and supplies. They can also be used for primary transport of certain products such as cedar shake blocks.*

The large payload with large helicopters is derived from high engine power that generates a strong downwash, which can cause breakage in the standing trees. Ground crews must be specially trained to work safely under such conditions.

Landing and storage space must be adequate for the safe operation of any size helicopter plus its support vehicles. The larger the helicopter, the larger the landing area required.

### ENVIRONMENTAL

Larger helicopters may be able to lift payloads out of difficult locations, such as gullies or canyons, that are beyond the lifting capability of smaller helicopters. This capability may make more areas available for salvage harvesting. However, larger helicopters also require more maneuvering room, and the stronger downwash may damage adjacent plantations or break branches and residual trees.

Falling can be done by either manual or mechanical methods: the choice between the two methods is driven primarily by terrain and timber characteristics. However, falling cannot be considered in isolation of the other phases because it helps to determine their efficiency and effectiveness. Trees must be felled and aligned in such a way as to minimize fibre loss, value loss, and site disturbance, and maximize productivity in a safe working environment.

One of the primary differences between hand-falling and mechanical falling is the effect on hookup efficiency. Hand-felled trees are hooked individually, but the bunching ability of mechanical falling equipment allows several trees to be hooked at a time.

The following section describes the characteristics of falling equipment, and how these characteristics affect the operational and environmental success of the falling equipment.

## Hand-falling

This activity dates back to the earliest history in the forest industry in British Columbia, and although the equipment has changed with lightweight, high-powered chainsaws, the physical aspects of the job remain similar. Falling trees is demanding activity that requires physical stamina, a concern for safety, and a regard to recovering the maximum value from each log.

**Figure 67**
*The faller must clear a safe path to move away from the tree when it starts to fall.*

A worker approaches each tree carrying a gasoline-powered chainsaw. The faller examines the tree to determine any safety hazards such as rotten limbs or tops, its direction of lean (trees are safest to fall in the direction of lean), and the proposed landing area. The faller prepares an escape route away from the proposed falling direction. The actual falling begins with a preliminary cut, called the undercut, on the side of the tree in the desired direction of falling, then a backcut above the undercut on the opposite side of the tree. A hinge of timber between the undercut and the backcut is left to control the tree during falling and to prevent the tree from splitting. When the backcut is almost complete and the tree starts to fall, the faller moves to a safe place on the escape route. After the tree is felled, it may be cut it into logs.

Hand-falling is often associated with large trees and steep or rough terrain — it is used for areas where ground-based machines cannot travel or where the trees are too large for mechanical falling equipment to handle effectively. Hand-falling is used more commonly on the Coast than in the Interior of British Columbia, although the proportion of hand-falling will decrease on the Coast as the amount of second-growth harvesting increases.

For simplicity, this section will discuss just the overall characteristics of hand-falling.

## Hand-falling is dangerous

Hand-falling is a dangerous occupation, and many workers are killed or injured each year in British Columbia as a result of falling accidents. Overhead hazards, precarious footing, and unstable logs that can slide over steep terrain all contribute to a hazardous work environment. Fallers must be aware of their surroundings at all times, and must always be prepared to protect themselves from hazards. Safety must be a primary concern for fallers: a thorough training program that emphasizes safety is essential for successful operations. Well-trained and productive fallers are a valuable asset to any operation.

Fallers must work with a partner to ensure that each worker has somebody nearby to periodically check on their safety. For small ground-based operations, the skidder operator may act as the partner if the terrain is suitable for simultaneous cut-and-skid operations. For larger operations, the partner is usually a faller as well, which means that the cutblock must be large enough to accommodate two or more fallers simultaneously. "Babysitters"— workers whose only function is to monitor the faller's safety — are used occasionally if the work area is too small to accommodate more than one faller.

Occupational safety regulations require at least two tree lengths between fallers. The space required between fallers increases with steeper terrain because trees may slide down the slope. Fallers cannot work above one another on steep slopes, and the space required to accommodate several fallers can be substantial. Therefore, the smaller cutblocks that have become more common in recent years require smaller falling crews. Falling costs increase with small crews because fixed costs such as transportation and supervision must be amortized over a lower production volume. Cutblocks on flatter ground can accommodate several fallers more easily because the trees do not slide.

Worker safety affects the starting place for falling on steep terrain. Trees tend to lean downhill, and cannot be felled uphill without a mechanical aid such as a hydraulic jack or winch. Furthermore, trees can slide downhill after cutting and could accumulate against the standing timber if falling were to start at the top of the cutblock, posing a safety hazard. Accordingly, falling must start at the lowest part of the cutblock, and proceed upslope across a "face" of timber oriented along the contour of the slope. The yarding that follows hand-falling usually cannot start until all the falling below the road is completed. The net result of the safety concern is that a higher level of the inventory must be carried between falling and yarding.

## Can work on difficult terrain

Hand-fallers can gain access to areas where mechanical falling equipment cannot operate; it is not uncommon for fallers on the Coast to work on slopes of 100% or more. Hand-falling is less common in the Interior, but is still used around steep-sided gullies, areas of large timber, and other areas that require special attention. With harvesting systems such as helicopters and large skylines, hand-falling is required because these systems are used only on difficult ground that ground-based equipment cannot access.

The amount of fibre recovery from cutblocks on difficult terrain must also be considered. Fallers usually fall the timber across the slope to minimize the amount of timber that "runs" down the slope and to maximize fibre recovery. When falling within gullies, the felled timber must be kept from sliding to the bottom of the gully, a difficult task on steep terrain. If the terrain is so rough as to preclude mechanical equipment and make access by hand-fallers difficult, then the amount of breakage may also be so high as to make the operation uneconomic. The ground must be examined in consideration of breakage during falling — large boulders or rock bluffs increase the potential for breakage.

### Not limited by tree size

Unlike mechanical falling equipment that is designed for a maximum tree size, hand-fallers are virtually unlimited by tree size. Chainsaws are available in various sizes and

**Figure 68**
*Large, old-growth timber felled by hand.*

power levels for cutting various-size trees. For large trees, chainsaws can be fitted with longer bars, and the faller can cut the tree from all sides; the chainsaw bar does not have to extend across the full width of the tree.

Small tree size affects productivity — not only for falling, but also for the subsequent phases. Trees are typically left unbunched after hand-falling (very small trees can be bunched by hand), which increases the extraction costs. Mechanical falling should be considered for smaller timber, depending on the amount of small timber and other site conditions.

### Falling and bucking can be done concurrently

Recovering the maximum value from each tree is an important factor in maximizing profitability, and the faller directly influences the amount of fibre recovered from each tree. A careful faller ensures that each tree is felled into the best landing zone to minimize breakage. In contrast, a careless faller can significantly increase breakage and value loss by not paying sufficient attention to the landing zone. Stumps, boulders, ridges, or logs oriented crossways to the falling direction can break an improperly felled tree.

**Figure 69**
*A faller preparing to buck a tree into logs.*

After the falling, the next step for maximizing the tree value is to "buck" it into logs of the correct length. On the Coast, where many trees are so large as to be unmanageable without bucking, one worker usually does both the falling and bucking. In the Interior, where tree-length or full-tree systems are more common, less bucking is done at the stump. Typical practice is to fall a few trees, and then buck them into logs, thus avoiding unbucked trees that are piled too high, rendering the bottom trees inaccessible.

Bucking for maximum value requires that the faller examine each tree thoroughly before deciding upon the best bucking locations. A set of corporate standards usually guides the faller, although some software programs are available for handheld computers to calculate the optimal bucking locations. The final decision always rests with the faller. Regardless of the means used to determine the bucking location, hand-falling and bucking provide the opportunity to examine each tree closely and to base the bucking decision on first-hand information.

Bucking large trees into logs can be difficult on steep, broken, or gullied terrain. The faller must be able to work safely, and the cuts must be positioned such that the resulting logs will not move after bucking. Logs shifting position after bucking can pose a significant safety hazard. If the terrain is unsuitable for at-the-stump bucking, then the yarding equipment must be large enough to handle the full-length trees without causing excessive breakage and soil disturbance.

Depending on corporate preferences, topping and limbing may be done at the stump or at roadside or landing. The location where debris accumulates may be an issue — topping and limbing the trees at the stump avoids the large accumulations of debris in the landing, but it may require more post-harvesting site treatments to abate the fire hazard or to create enough plantable sites. Even with at-the-stump bucking, broken ends usually remain and require trimming at the landing, so roadside accumulations cannot be avoided altogether.

## Capital costs, operating costs, and productivity are low

The capital investment required for hand-falling is several hundred times less than for mechanical falling, and the falling cost per cubic metre is usually lower as well. Despite these differences, other factors such as terrain and timber conditions and total system productivity dominate the choice between the two systems for large contractors. Hand-falling is unsuitable to use with highly mechanized skidding equipment such as grapple skidders and clambunks because of its lower productivity, both for the falling and for the subsequent extraction phase.

However, capital costs are an important factor for smaller or part-time contractors who may be unable to amortize the costs over a large volume. Hand-falling is often associated with contractors specialized in operations such as steep-slope or sensitive-ground areas.

## Affected by weather

Inclement weather affects hand-fallers more than mechanical falling equipment. It is not uncommon on the Coast to lose several days' work each year because of high wind, snow, or fog, especially during the fall and winter.

Even though the fallers may be unable to work for a particular day, some labour costs could still be incurred because of the terms of collective labour agreements, thus increasing the falling costs for the entire cutblock. Having alternative work sites, such as a nearby cutblock in different weather conditions will help to alleviate the cost of lost workdays. Weather conditions, especially high winds, are often localized; it may be

**Figure 70**
*Shovelling may be required to remove deep snow from around the trees.*

possible to find an alternate work site with suitable weather conditions, provided that the required cutting approvals are in place.

### Stump height must be controlled

The faller must bend over to reach as close to the ground as possible to keep the stump heights within tolerances. Fallers must be in top physical condition to perform this task continually.

Furthermore, in the Interior where operations on deep snow are common, the fallers may be unable to get the stumps low enough without shovelling the snow away from the tree. It is not uncommon to hire extra workers to remove the snow from around the trees to avoid too-high stumps.

**Figure 71**
*This hand-felled timber was in a partial cut helicopter block on steep terrain in the Queen Charlotte Islands.*

### Can work in clearcut or partial cut

Hand-falling can be done both for partial cutting and clearcutting, in both old-growth and second-growth stands. Compared with mechanical falling, hand-falling has both advantages and disadvantages in a partial cut.

A faller on foot is more mobile than a machine. Because no trail is required, the faller can approach any tree without regard to whether the crop trees could accidentally be damaged by a careless movement. Furthermore, by approaching close to each tree, the faller can examine it to confirm whether it should be harvested — such a decision may be easier adjacent to the tree rather than 5–7 m away in a machine's cab.

On the other hand, hand-falling in closed or decadent stands is difficult because of the increased safety hazard. Trees can become entangled in the limbs of adjacent trees, and rotten tops or limbs can pose a significant overhead hazard. Every tree is like the first tree felled in a clearcut, which is one of the most dangerous phases of falling. Lastly, the faller cannot reposition the trees after falling, and therefore must ensure that they are oriented correctly with the proposed direction of skidding or yarding. Poor control of the falling direction can increase the extraction costs significantly.

Partial cutting in steep coastal old-growth cutblocks with large, high-volume trees has often been thought to be too dangerous to consider. However, recent studies by FERIC have successfully demonstrated this technique (Bennett 1997). Partial cutting is more common in coastal second-growth forests and in the Interior, where the trees are smaller and more thrifty, and the terrain less difficult.

## Mechanical Falling

Mechanical falling equipment eliminates the need for a worker on the ground — instead of a worker with a chainsaw cutting each tree manually, a ground-based machine equipped with a felling head does the work. This factor significantly increases worker safety, reduces the physical demands on the worker, improves fibre utilization, and allows different equipment to be used for extraction.

The typical mechanical falling equipment used in British Columbia consists of an excavator-based carrier with a falling attachment such as a hydraulically driven disc or chainsaw. Typical falling machines can reach trees 5–7 m or more from their counterpoint and cut a swath 10–12 m wide on each pass. The machines usually travel just one time over each path. After the trees are cut from the stump, they can either be bunched to facilitate extraction, or simply directed towards the preferred landing zone.

A wide variety of mechanical falling equipment is available. The common and distinguishing characteristics of these machines will be discussed separately.

## Common Features of Mechanized Falling Equipment

Besides replacing an on-the-ground worker with a machine, all mechanical falling equipment share some additional characteristics. They all can move the logs after falling, have an operator enclosed in a protective cab, can work in clearcuts or partial cuts, and are expensive to own and operate. The following section will discuss how each of these features affects the operational and environmental risks for the machines.

### Large machine travels to each tree

A large machine is required to carry the felling head to each tree. As with ground-based skidding equipment, access is constrained by slope, terrain, and soil strength, and soil disturbance may be caused.

OPERATIONAL

Mechanical falling equipment is limited to the terrain and slope that it can travel over. Track-mounted machines can work on slopes up to 60%, and some specialized machines can work on steeper slopes. However, rubber-tired falling equipment is limited to much lower slopes. Windfalls, large boulders, depressions, and rock bluffs are typical obstacles that must be moved or avoided.

**Figure 72**

*A large feller-buncher with tilt-cab, zero-clearance tailswing, and high-speed disc saw. This machine was operating in the transition zone between coastal and interior conditions.*

In clearcuts on gentle terrain, the equipment usually travels back and forth across the slope, cutting a swath on each pass. Cutting begins at the top of the slope so that the trees can be bunched into the clearing with the butts pointing downhill. On steeper terrain, the preferred travel direction is straight up and down the slopes to enhance machine stability. The trees are bunched to the side. On very steep terrain, machines fall the trees while travelling upslope, then return to the bottom of the slope without cutting, and then start another swath.

ENVIRONMENTAL

Soil disturbance is less of an issue with mechanical falling equipment than with skidding equipment because of the fewer passes over the ground and the lower travel speed. However, even single passes of a machine can cause soil disturbance if the soil is susceptible to compaction (e.g., fine-textured or wet soils). Heavy equipment should be used under more favourable conditions (e.g., coarse soil or dry, frozen, or deep snowpack conditions).

The felling head must be aligned straight-on with the tree before cutting. With boom-mounted fellers, the boom or superstructure simply turns to face the tree, but drive-to-tree machines must be re-positioned to align with the tree. Such movement may cause soil disturbance. Boom-mounted fellers may require more turning for proper positioning on steep ground.

**Figure 73**
*Piling trees into bunches with a typical feller-buncher.*

### Can move the tree after cutting

All mechanical falling equipment has some capability for moving the trees after falling. Feller-bunchers are designed specifically for this task, while feller-directors move the trees only incidentally after falling. Feller-processors cut the trees and pile the logs as they are produced.

**OPERATIONAL**

The ability to place the trees into bunches enhances the productivity of the extraction phase by reducing the hookup time. This single feature of mechanical felling equipment allows machines such as grapple skidders and clambunks to achieve their high productivity levels.

**ENVIRONMENTAL**

Falling equipment can be used to move trees away from sensitive areas such as riparian zones, perhaps with less risk than using the skidding equipment. Mechanical falling equipment travels more slowly than skidding equipment, and has a lower risk of causing soil disturbance. Once piled away from the sensitive area, the trees can be skidded to the landing with less risk of the skidder causing soil disturbance.

### Operator is enclosed in a cab

Mechanical falling equipment elevates the faller off the ground into the comfort of a

**Figure 74**
*The root wads from windfallen trees pose a safety hazard. Mechanical falling is much safer than hand-falling under these conditions.*

machine's cab, not only making the work less strenuous, but also enhancing safety.

**OPERATIONAL**

Once enclosed in the protective cab of a machine, the faller's safety is greatly enhanced. Rotten tops and branches no longer pose a safety concern, and trees that become entangled in the limbs of other trees can be moved without endangering the faller. Windfalls can be handled without exposing the faller to the danger of root wads that might overturn after cutting, or to the potentially lethal energy stored in bent and highly stressed stems.

The physical demands of the job are also reduced as compared with hand-falling, which may or may not be a benefit depending on the individual's preferences. Both jobs require highly skilled people, but their skill requirements are not interchangeable and each attracts workers from a different labour pool.

Nighttime operations are feasible because of the reduced safety hazards. Falling and other phases typically proceed around the clock in many highly mechanized operations in the Interior.

### ENVIRONMENTAL

Being some distance from the tree being cut and enclosed in a cab, the operator's vision may be impaired compared with that of a hand-faller. This may make choosing the correct trees to cut and leave in partial cutting prescriptions more difficult, especially if the difference between cut and leave trees is subtle. The vision problem is worse during nighttime operations since the lights do not illuminate the tree tops, and it may be difficult to distinguish the correct trees from the bottom alone. Pre-marking the trees can make it easier for the machine operator to select the correct trees for falling, but at the cost of an additional crew.

### Can work in clearcut or partial cut

Mechanical falling equipment can be used for partial cutting as well as clearcutting; however, a series of corridors must be cleared to provide access to all parts of the stand. The same corridors are used later for extraction. Boom-mounted machines reach from the corridor between the residual trees to the harvested trees, although they are limited by the length of the boom. Purpose-built feller-processors usually have a longer reach than machines adapted from feller-bunchers, so the access corridors can be spaced wider apart. Drive-to-tree machines must have free access to all the trees to be harvested.

**Figure 75**
*A zero-clearance, tilt-cab feller-buncher working in a selection cut.*

The operators must be careful not to damage the residual trees, and a design feature of classic excavator-based fellers makes them particularly susceptible to this problem. The superstructure overhangs the tracks when the machine is turned sideways, and the overhang is out of the operator's line of vision. It would be quite easy to knock over the trees adjacent to a narrow corridor. Some excavator-based fellers have a "zero-clearance" tailswing design to eliminate this problem. Drive-to-tree fellers require sufficient space to turn towards the trees without damaging the residual trees.

If a tree becomes entangled in the surrounding trees during falling, it can simply be dislodged without endangering the machine operator.

## Capital costs, operating costs, and productivity are high

The owning and operating costs of mechanical falling equipment are much higher than for hand-falling. The high ownership costs make it vital to provide enough volume of timber over the entire operating season to keep the equipment busy and to amortize the capital costs at a reasonable rate. The high operating costs compared with hand-falling make it vital to recover the extra costs in another phase (i.e., extraction). The bunching ability and high productivity of the mechanical falling equipment make it feasible to use highly productive skidding equipment such as grapple skidders and clambunks. Bunching can also improve the productivity for cable systems, especially swing yarders configured for grapple yarding. Without the cost savings for these phases, the extra costs for mechanical falling equipment would not be warranted.

These factors work together to make mechanical falling equipment suitable for large, full-time contractors, and unsuitable for smaller, part-time operators.

## Distinguishing Features of Mechanized Falling Equipment

Five major characteristics distinguish the various types of mechanical falling equipment from one another: the method for advancing the felling head to the tree, the carrier type, the machine function, the machine's size, and the type of felling head. In addition, several other important features to be discussed here may be found on a particular make and model.

### Boom-mounted and drive-to-tree

The felling head must be positioned next to the tree before cutting, either by a boom or by driving the carrier to the tree. The most common type used in British Columbia is boom mounted, although some drive-to-tree machines are used. Drive-to-tree machines are limited to operating on excellent soil and terrain conditions because they must literally be driven to each tree. Their ideal operating conditions consist of flat ground with no obstacles. On the other hand, boom-mounted fellers remain at some distance from the tree during the cutting cycle, with just the cutting head approaching the tree. These machines depend less on favourable terrain.

*Boom-mounted* Boom-mounted fellers are not hampered by the same terrain limitations as drive-to-tree machines because the carrier remains about

**Figure 76**
*Piling trees into bunches with a typical feller-buncher with a heavy-duty boom. The high-speed disc saw is visible at the bottom of the felling head.*

**Figure 77**
*A light-duty, knuckle boom. This boom design is intended for falling, not for heavy lifting.*

3–10 m away from the tree. The felling head usually rotates side-to-side relative to the boom by about 20 degrees or more to reduce the impact of leaning trees or uneven ground. See the "High-rotation head" section for additional information.

**Figure 78**
*A telescopic boom allows for compact size as well as longer reach.*

Two types of booms are used: heavy-duty and light-duty. Heavy-duty booms are typical of feller-bunchers, and are intended for full-tree operations where the entire tree is lifted. On the other hand, booms on felling equipment used in cut-to-length operations are usually longer and lighter because they are not intended for lifting the entire tree. Two different designs are seen: knuckle booms and telescopic slide-booms. The telescopic booms combine long reach and compact size at the expense of mechanical complexity.

The exact work cycle will vary depending on the type of boom and harvesting head, but it begins by positioning the carrier within reaching distance of the trees. Trees are selected individually, and cut from the stump. With feller-bunchers, the trees are held vertically before they are dropped into a bunch, usually behind the machine. With light-duty booms on feller-processors and feller-directors, the tree's falling direction is simply controlled by orienting the felling head properly on the tree before starting the cut. Once the cut is completed, the tree usually falls into the residual stand. Once on the ground, the tree is cut into logs in the case of feller-processors or possibly shifted into a bunch with a feller-director.

After cutting all the trees within its reach, the machine advances to the next cutting location, and repeats the process.

### OPERATIONAL

Boom-mounted felling heads facilitate bunching. Trees can be moved from the stump to a bunch by simply turning the boom or superstructure instead of repositioning the entire machine.

Slope limits the operating range for boom-mounted fellers, both from the perspective of machine stability as well as the maximum slope at which the boom can be swivelled. Turning the machine on a slope while carrying a heavy payload requires more power than on flat land. To compensate, the working radius is reduced to less than the maximum extension.

The shorter reach of heavy-duty booms means that the machine must spend a higher proportion of its operating time moving between trees.

### ENVIRONMENTAL

Boom-mounted machines do not require turning at each cutting site — the felling head is aligned by swivelling the superstructure or the boom itself. Soil disturbance is reduced.

Boom-mounted fellers can reach into a stand to cut an individual tree more easily than a drive-to-tree feller. This feature can be beneficial along riparian zones or similar areas where individual trees must be removed without affecting the residual stand.

With heavy-duty booms, trees are held vertically after cutting, and debris such as broken limbs is likely to fall on the cab. This has two implications: the carrier's cab must be designed to withstand the abuse, and the accumulating debris tends to obscure the operator's vision. Both factors tend to limit the overhead visibility; consequently, the boom design should be considered where trees require careful examination before cutting, such as in partial cuts. With light-duty booms using feller-processor heads, the debris tends to fall away from the cab, thus not accumulating on the roof where it could obscure visibility.

***Drive-to-tree***   Drive-to-tree carriers can be either tracked or wheeled, and the wheeled carriers can be either three- or four-wheel designs. Although none of them is used extensively in British Columbia, they are used commonly in other regions, and are included here for reference.

Three-wheel fellers with a castering rear wheel are quick and highly maneuverable; however, they cannot carry as large trees as other, more stable carriers. Four-wheel carriers are less maneuverable than the three-wheel machines, but more stable.

See the "Ground-based Primary Transport" section for a discussion of the differences between wheeled and tracked carriers.

### OPERATIONAL

Drive-to-tree felling machines feature simpler design and construction than boom-mounted machines, and are more economical to own and operate under favourable operating conditions. However, obstacles such as windfalls, boulders, or depressions can prevent drive-to-tree machines from engaging the trees, or they can render the machines uneconomic because of the time required to clear the obstacles. Such obstacles near the tree might prevent the felling head from being fully lowered, which may result in higher stumps and less fibre recovery. The machines could also become unstable when driving over uneven ground while transporting a tree. Operator comfort is reduced compared with boom-mounted machines because of the increased travel over rough terrain.

*Figure 79*
*A three-wheeled feller-buncher. This type of carrier requires highly favourable ground conditions to be used successfully.*

The castering wheel on the three-wheeled machines provides them with a very tight turning radius — they can travel between a straight row of planted trees then easily turn perpendicular to the row to face the trees for cutting.

Tracked machines are typically slower and heavier than wheeled machines and can carry a larger felling head.

### ENVIRONMENTAL

Drive-to-tree machines may cause more soil disturbance because they must be turned to face each tree before cutting. Also, soil compaction can be greater because the machines often travel several times over a given area.

## Carriers for boom-mounted felling heads

The boom-mounted fellers can be divided into two groups based on the carrier type. Excavator-based carriers have tracks and a rotating superstructure. Articulated, rubber-tired carriers are similar to the carriers used for forwarders, but their construction is generally lighter because they are not designed to support the tree's entire weight during falling and processing.

*Excavator-based* The original excavator-based felling machines were simply conversions of standard excavators, but now these machines are usually constructed on purpose-built carriers. Some designs may bear little resemblance to conventional excavators, with features such as zero-clearance tailswing or tilting cabs, both of which will be discussed later.

**Figure 80**
*A typical feller-buncher. While similar to an excavator in overall appearance, special features of the cab, boom, undercarriage, and body protection distinguish this machine as one optimized for falling.*

### OPERATIONAL

Excavator-based carriers can operate on a wide range of terrain and soil conditions. Their robust construction and stability allow them to travel on fairly steep sections such as near gullies and broken ground. It is not uncommon for excavator-based fellers to operate on short pitches up to 60%, and some special designs can operate up to 70%.

### ENVIRONMENTAL

Excavator-based fellers have a fairly light footprint, especially since they normally travel just one time over each section of ground and do a limited amount of turning. Adverse soil impacts are more likely to be caused by the extraction phase than by the falling equipment.

Situations could arise where the impact of mechanical falling equipment could exceed the impact of the extraction equipment, and the impact of the falling equipment must be managed separately. For example, cable yarding could be required because of terrain conditions such as sensitive soil, yet mechanical falling might still be feasible because the slope is within limits. Under these conditions, the falling might be required to occur during dry or frozen conditions to minimize the impact of the falling equipment.

The size and configuration of the machine can affect its usefulness for partial cutting. Unless designed with a zero-clearance tailswing, the superstructure overhang can damage the residual trees close to the access corridor in a partial cut.

*Articulated, rubber-tired carrier* These carriers are typically used as feller-processors in the cut-to-length system; it is difficult to separate the effects of the carrier from those of the felling head and the entire harvesting system. These two issues will be discussed later in the handbook.

Rubber-tired carriers are similar to forwarders, but with a boom instead of a log cradle. As with forwarders, they can be fitted with tracks over the wheels to increase the

**Figure 81**
*An articulated, rubber-tired carrier with three axles and track-and-tire tractive system. Note the lightweight protection and large windows typical of Scandinavian designs.*

footprint area and reduce the ground pressure. The operator's cab is normally mounted in a fixed position, although some carriers use a swivel mounting.

### OPERATIONAL

The equipment is expensive to purchase and is less productive than typical North American fellers. However, these features are more characteristic of the entire CTL system than just of the carrier. See the discussion in the "Operating Techniques" section about the various harvesting systems.

Being rubber-tire mounted, these carriers can quickly move between operating areas without requiring a low-bed.

### ENVIRONMENTAL

Since these machines are most often used as feller-processors, they usually travel on a mat of limbs and tops. In addition, the longer boom typical of these carriers can reach farther from the trail, allowing wider trail spacing. Considering these factors with their low ground pressure, these carriers cause little soil disturbance while travelling.

Articulated, rubber-tired carriers typically have a more "high-tech" design than excavator-based carriers, including larger windows for improved visibility, which can be an asset for working in thinning or partial cutting operations.

### Felling head

Felling heads can be grouped into four classes. Feller-bunchers cut the trees and pile them into bunches, while directors just cut the trees, leaving them on the ground where

**Figure 82**
*A typical feller-buncher head. This head has a low-speed saw mounted on a sliding carriage. It also features accumulator arms that cut and hold several trees simultaneously.*

they fall. Feller-processor heads, both single-grip and double-grip, cut the trees and then manufacture them into logs. Single-grip feller-processors perform both actions with just one head, whereas double-grip feller-processors require two components to accomplish the task.

The choice between the four types depends mainly on the wood form desired for the extraction phase, as well as the timber characteristics in the operating area.

***Feller-buncher*** Feller-bunchers are the most common type of felling head used in British Columbia. They are highly productive, and well suited to working with high-productivity skidding equipment such as grapple skidders and clambunks. They must be mounted on a robust carrier that can withstand the stresses caused by lifting and moving whole trees.

Some of the distinguishing characteristics

between the different makes and models of feller-buncher heads are the size, the type of saw, and whether the feller-buncher can hold several trees simultaneously (i.e., has accumulator arms).

Feller-bunchers are available in a range of sizes as determined by the maximum opening size. The smallest feller-bunchers can cut and hold trees up to about 40 cm in diameter, while the largest feller-bunchers have openings of about 70 cm. For the occasional large trees, feller-bunchers can cut the tree from both sides, effectively increasing the maximum tree size. Oversize trees are usually just felled, without trying to hold the tree for bunching.

Most feller-bunchers use circular saw blades, either continuous high-speed or intermittent low-speed, although some older models use cone saws, augers, or chainsaws.

The saw blade in high-speed saws spins continuously when operating, and the kinetic energy stored in the disc provides the power for cutting. To start the cutting cycle, the felling head is positioned in front of the tree without actually touching it. When the operator is ready to begin cutting, the head is advanced quickly and smoothly into the tree. Cutting time is less than one second. After the tree is completely severed, the grapple arms close around the tree to prevent it from falling. The operator must be highly coordinated to advance the blade through the tree without stalling it and to grasp the tree before it begins to fall. If the saw fails to cut the tree completely, then the head must be withdrawn, the saw blade spun up to full speed, and the process repeated.

The "cut-before-hold" procedure ensures that the head does not bend the tree and induce any stresses that may cause the wood to shatter or split. Very cold weather may cause the wood to split more easily.

High-speed saws are best suited for smaller-diameter trees since they rely on quick cutting.

With low-speed saws, the blade rotates only when it is actually cutting the tree. The blade is mounted on a sliding carriage that allows the felling head to fully grasp the tree when the blade is in the retracted position. Once the grapple arms are closed, the saw blade is advanced, usually taking three to five seconds to cut through the tree. Motor power, not kinetic energy, is used to cut the tree, so low-speed saws can be used on larger-diameter trees. They are not well suited to small-diameter trees because of their lower productivity.

These high-speed and low-speed saw heads are designed and constructed quite ruggedly, and are often used to knock down undersized, non-merchantable trees. They are also effective for cutting heavily limbed trees.

All feller-buncher heads have grapple arms for holding the trees both during the cutting and bunching stages. Some felling heads are equipped with accumulator arms that allow the head to cut and hold several trees before bunching to increase productivity.

To minimize the amount of turning and soil disturbance, the bunches must be

**Figure 83**
*Feller-director head used for coastal second-growth timber. After falling, the trees can be moved by lifting them with the grapple arms.*

aligned with the intended skidding direction, so the feller-buncher operator must be aware of the skidding plans. In stands of small trees, several trees can be cut and accumulated in the felling head before turning to deposit the trees in a bunch. With larger trees, they are cut and bunched individually. Bunches typically contain 5–10 trees.

***Feller-director*** A feller-director is used to fall trees in a preferred direction. Bunching can be done with directors by shifting the trees' locations after they are felled. By not lifting the full weight of the trees, directors can be mounted on smaller carriers than required for conventional bunching.

The original felling heads used in British Columbia were drive-to-tree feller-directors using shears. Shears act like scissors, are simple to use and inexpensive to manufacture. Unfortunately, they also cause significant damage to the trees by crushing the fibre and splitting or shattering the wood. Such damage is especially significant during cold weather. Since almost all British Columbia operations produce sawlogs, and their value is reduced significantly by such damage, shears are rarely used in British Columbia. Shears can be used successfully in regions where pulp logs are the primary product because the damage caused to the trees does not devalue the product.

Boom-mounted directors typically use chainsaws for cutting. The use of chainsaws allows the weight of the felling head to be kept low, which subsequently allows the use of a lighter carrier. The felling heads on double-grip feller-processors are actually chainsaw feller-directors.

***Feller-processor: single grip and double grip*** Feller-processors combine the falling and log-manufacturing functions into one machine. Single-grip feller-processors use a single, boom-mounted head for both the falling and manufacturing, while double-grip feller-processors have separate falling and processing heads.

**Figure 84**
*A single-grip feller-processor with a non-rigid mounting. This tree was just felled, and is now being cut into short logs. The logs are sorted into different piles according to their grade.*

**Figure 85**
*This double-grip feller-processor has a boom-mounted felling head and a chassis-mounted processing head.*

The essential components in a typical single-grip feller-processor head include a chainsaw for cutting, powered rollers for feeding the tree through the processor, delimbing knives, and encoders for measuring diameter and length. Some models uses a stroke principle instead of powered rollers for moving the logs, but these machines are limited to cutting fixed lengths. In double-grip feller-processors, the felling head is essentially a lightweight feller-director, while the processor itself has a second chainsaw, powered rollers, delimbing knives, and measuring devices. These components are similar to those in a single-grip feller-processor, only larger and mounted on the carrier instead of the felling head.

The log manufacturing functions in feller-processors are usually controlled by a computer that allows the operator to specify various size limits for cutting the logs. Accuracy and reliability of the length-measuring system is critical for these machines to be used successfully, especially in cut-to-length operations. See the "Log-measurement methods" discussion in the "Processing Equipment" section for further information.

Single-grip feller-processors are better suited to smaller timber, while double-grip feller-processors can work with larger timber. Double-grip machines are better suited in dense understorey because they can penetrate the brush more easily than single-grip feller-processors. They can also be used with feller-bunchers, where they would perform only the processing function.

**Figure 86**
*A single-grip feller-processor head.*

Single-grip feller-processors are relatively delicate machines that cannot withstand as much abuse as feller-bunchers. As a result, the head cannot be pushed as easily through deep snow to cut low stumps, and the head cannot be used to simply knock over undersized trees. Consequently, every tree must be cut individually, but once cut, only a little extra processing time is required to produce a log. Fewer trees are discarded, and single-grip feller-processors may be able to extract more timber from a given stand than a feller-buncher. Feller-processors may also be less effective falling heavily limbed trees than feller-bunchers.

**Figure 87**
*The levelling cab allows for easier operations on steep terrain. The engine is located in the lower module, below the operator's cab.*

**Levelling cab**
When boom-mounted fellers work on steep ground, their lifting capacity is reduced because of the power requirements for turning the machine with a

**Figure 88**
*A conventional feller-buncher mounted on hydraulic levelling cylinders. This design provides less levelling adjustment than the other designs.*

payload — the superstructure tends to swing downhill under the force of gravity. Furthermore, tilting the cab too steeply makes it very uncomfortable for the operator. Mounting the cab and boom on a platform that compensates for the ground slope can alleviate both of these problems.

The additional hardware required to provide the levelling capability increases the weight of the machine, which can increase the ground pressure. Mechanical complexity and capital costs are also higher.

**Figure 89**
*A zero-clearance levelling feller-processor with levelling cab. The engine is located beside the cab.*

### Zero-clearance tail swing

The superstructure of a conventional excavator overhangs the tracks when the machine is turned sideways, which could easily cause damage to the trees adjacent to a narrow corridor. The zero-clearance design eliminates this problem by reducing the length of the cab behind the pivot point. These machines can work and travel easily within a corridor only as wide as their nominal width. However, the design also means that the counter-balancing provided by the overhang is eliminated, which reduces the machine's lifting capacity.

### Size

The mechanical falling equipment should be matched to the expected size of the timber. In addition, the overall width of the carrier can be significant in partial cutting operations where narrow corridors are important.

**Figure 90**
*The high-rotation mechanism for a feller-buncher head.*

The largest feller-bunchers can handle coastal second-growth timber and some coastal old growth by cutting the trees from two sides. The smallest feller-bunchers are suitable for uniform stands such as the pine stands in the central Interior of British Columbia.

### High-rotation head

A recent innovation for feller-buncher heads is to mount them on a swivel that provides about 250 degrees of movement, compared with about 20 degrees for a conventional feller-buncher. This design makes it easier to align the head in directions other than "straight ahead." Some benefits of this design are that the head can be aligned with heavily leaning trees and windfalls lying at odd angles, the bunches can be aligned at different angles than straight away from the feller-buncher, and the larger bunches improve skidding productivity.

The net result is that the feller-buncher can either retrieve or place bunches at odd angles without having to reposition the carrier. This feature can improve productivity and reduce the amount of soil disturbance.

**Rigid attachment to boom**

Feller-buncher heads are attached rigidly to the boom so that the trees can be held vertically after they are cut from the stump. In contrast, most feller-processor heads are not designed to hold the tree vertically after cutting — the tree simply falls in the direction that the head is pointed. Feller-processor heads cannot be used effectively for bunching other than for piling the short logs.

**Figure 91**

*A feller-processor head with a rigid mounting to the boom, making it suitable for use as a feller-buncher or a processor. Note the robust carrier and boom compared with other feller-processors. The head also has a high-rotation side-tilt mechanism that allows for piling of logs beside the machine.*

## PROCESSING EQUIPMENT

The term "processing" is used generically to include any action applied to the trees after they are felled and before they are delivered to the mill. Processing typically involves cutting trees into logs that meet the requirements of the secondary transport system and the mills. Common functions include cutting the logs to specific lengths, topping, trimming branches, and removing defects such as rot, spiral grain, and forks. As used here, "processing" also includes debarking, chipping, or slashing at sites other than at mills.

Like falling, the processing phase can be conducted manually or mechanically, and also like falling, the timber characteristics play a large role in the choice between the two methods. For most coastal old-growth stands and some sites in the Interior, the trees are simply too large for typical mechanical processing equipment, therefore manual methods must be used. On the other hand, mechanical processing is standard practice for many Interior sites, and is becoming more common for coastal second-growth sites. Terrain plays only a minor role in the choice between the manual and mechanical processing methods — its influence on falling and extraction methods is more pronounced.

In the choice between manual and mechanical processing methods, the interaction between the phases is more important than terrain. For example, the processing capacity should be matched to the other phases' productivities, the equipment must be suitable to accept the timber as presented by the extraction phase, and it must present the processed logs to the loading phase as efficiently as possible. Mechanical processing equipment has much higher productive capacity than manual processing, but it also carries higher ownership costs. The productivity of the whole system must be high enough to amortize the higher fixed costs at an acceptable rate.

The following sections describe the characteristics for processing equipment, and how these characteristics affect its operational and environmental success.

### Hand-bucking

Hand-processing, or "bucking," consists of cutting trees into logs of specified length and diameter classes using a chainsaw. Hand-bucking is usually associated with large timber or low-production systems, and is more common on the Coast than in the Interior. If the timber is hand-felled, it is also likely to be hand-processed.

Bucking is usually done on the landing or roadside before the logs are loaded onto the trucks; therefore, it must be well coordinated to blend between extraction and

**Figure 92**
*A landing bucker working in a coastal cutblock.*

loading without delaying either of these phases. The bucker must be aware of all machines working in the vicinity, and the machine operators must be aware of the bucker's location at all times to avoid accidents. The risk of accidents increases any time that people work on the ground near heavy equipment.

The trees are spread out on the ground, which allows the worker to determine their size and quality. The trees are measured with a tape, then cut to the proper length, and tops and branches are removed. Any unacceptable defects such as broken or shattered ends, rot, and crook are trimmed from the logs. After the logs are removed for storage or loading, the skidder or loader removes the debris and piles it away from the work area.

## Bucking can occur in various locations

Bucking can take place at the stump, at roadside or landing, or in a central landing. In many coastal operations, the faller bucks the trees into logs that can be handled more easily by the extraction equipment — see the section on hand-falling for further information. Even when the faller does the initial bucking, a landing bucker is often required to remove defects overlooked or inaccessible to the faller. On the other hand, if the faller performs no bucking, then a landing bucker is required.

The challenge with roadside bucking is to provide the bucker with access to all the trees — only the top tier is accessible without help. Consequently, the bucker must work with a loader or other machine. Typical procedure is for the loader to place several logs on the road, then wait for the bucker to be finished. Consequently, the loader is limited to the production rate of the bucker and the bucker cannot work any faster than the loader. Both characteristics are diametrically opposed to the concept of having each phase work at its own best rate to minimize costs.

In landing operations when bucking and loading happen at the same time as extraction, proper planning ensures maximum productivity and safety. Reducing the delay times for the extraction equipment is especially important, and landings are often organized with a specific area for the extraction equipment to drop the logs then return quickly to the cutblock. The bucker must keep clear of this zone when the extraction equipment is near the landing.

Hand-bucking can be especially difficult with cable systems on steep terrain. For example, environmental regulations and construction costs limit the landing size, making it difficult to provide adequate space to park the yarder, loader, and log truck and still leave enough room to process and stockpile the logs. One technique is to process the logs in the loading zone while the log trucks are absent, which limits the available productive time for the bucker. An alternative is to forward the logs with a skidder to an adjacent landing away from the yarder. Safety is also a concern on small landings — the "pinch zone" between the yarder and loader is a very hazardous location for any on-the-ground worker. The machines must be positioned carefully to ensure that the gap between them is always large enough to meet safety regulations.

Hand-bucking on landings for ground-based equipment may be easier because there are fewer machines on the landing, there are more options on where to place the incoming trees, and the terrain is usually less severe. However, proper organization ensures that the bucker keeps clear of the skidder and loader at all times, for reasons of both safety and productivity.

Hand-bucking in central processing yards is normally a final upgrading procedure to maximize the value derived from the logs. Since the traffic is often heavy in central yards, strict procedures must be established to ensure safe working conditions.

## Bucker can view the logs at close range

With hand-bucking, every log can be examined closely to detect any subtle defects, and can be viewed from all sides if required. Such close viewing can be an advantage compared with mechanical processing where the logs are viewed at a distance. On the other hand, the bucker seldom has any mechanical aids to help determine the log grade, and must usually rely on his experience and knowledge, guided by a set of corporate standards. Some programs are available for handheld computers to calculate the optimal bucking locations, but are rarely used in British Columbia.

### Capital costs and productivity are low

Like hand-falling, the capital investment for hand-bucking is low, requiring only a chainsaw, measuring tape, corporate bucking standards, and safety equipment. However, the low capital costs carry the limitations of low productivity and safety hazards. A chainsaw being operated close to legs and feet always presents a safety risk.

Low productivity with buckers may not be an issue if the productivity matches the other phases. If more production is required to match the other phases, and where room is available to establish additional safe workplaces, more buckers can be added easily.

## Mechanical Processing

Mechanical processing equipment elevates the bucker off the ground, with all the safety benefits of enclosing a worker in a protective cab. As well, productivity is increased, allowing the economic benefits of higher-capacity machines in the extraction and loading phases to be realized.

Many types of mechanical processing equipment are available, although not all are commonly used in British Columbia. The dangle-head processors and stroke delimbers are widely used in both roadside and landing operations, as are feller-processors, a variation of the dangle-head processor. Less common are pull-through delimbers, slashers, and "tray-based" processors. Other machines such as chain-flail delimbers and chippers are used for specialty operations.

These machines share some characteristics that apply to processors as a whole, as well as other characteristics that distinguish the various machines from one another. These characteristics will be discussed in the next two sections.

### Common Features of Mechanized Processing Equipment

In general, mechanized processing equipment is faster and safer than hand-buckers, and the machines can be used at night for round-the-clock operations. They almost always have the ability to sort the logs, and they can be computerized to help with log measurement and bucking decisions. This section will discuss how each of these features affects the operational and environmental risks for the machines.

**Figure 93**
*A stroke delimber working on a roadside log deck. These machines can process up to three trees per minute, with the operator fully enclosed in a protective cab.*

#### Faster, safer, and more capital intensive than hand-bucking

As with falling, the introduction of a machine into the processing function increases productivity and reduces the safety hazard — an on-the-ground worker is no longer required to work near heavy equipment on a

**Figure 94**
*A dangle-head processor working from a roadside pile. Trees are pulled from the large deck on the right, and the processed logs are piled to the left of the machine.*

busy landing. Instead, the worker is enclosed in a protective cab, free from the risk of being cut by a chainsaw or being struck by another machine.

High-productivity skidders and loaders require mechanical processing equipment as part of the harvesting system because hand-buckers are unable to keep up — the higher productive capacity of the skidders and loaders would be wasted without mechanical processing. Not only is mechanical processing equipment more productive on a per-hour basis, but it also increases the number of available working hours per day. With the operator enclosed in a cab, processors can work at night, allowing for higher machine utilization.

However, the capital costs for most mechanical processors are also significantly higher compared with hand-bucking. This higher productivity is not only possible, but is required to amortize the equipment at an acceptable cost. Most mechanical processing equipment is unsuitable for low production; see the description of pull-through delimbers for an exception.

### Processor can move logs for sorting
Mechanical processing equipment can usually move logs both before and after processing, which allows the equipment to be separated from the skidding or loading phases. Each machine can work at its own pace, without interference from the other phases — such separation is often impractical with hand-buckers because they cannot pull the logs out of the piles for processing.

The processors can also sort the logs as part of their normal function, although the number of sorts is usually limited to four or less. Limiting factors for the number of sorts include the amount of space available for the different products, reduced productivity while sorting, and the relative volume of each sort — complete truckloads of each sort are usually required for efficient loading and hauling. Although most processors can sort to some degree, they differ in their sorting efficiency, as will be discussed later.

### Mechanical aids are available for length and diameter measurements
Most recent mechanical processing equipment can measure the log dimensions, either by digital encoders or fixed-length benchmarks built into the machine. Length measurement is most common, while some more sophisticated machines can also measure diameters. A computer can be used to optimize the bucking decisions, or the raw information can simply be displayed for the operator to make the decision.

However, the measurements do not come without cost — both for purchasing and operation. The extra hardware needs to be operated properly and calibrated regularly to ensure accuracy, and it may be prone to failure.

# Distinguishing Features of Mechanized Processing Equipment

There are several distinct classes of processing equipment, including the stroke delimbers and dangle-head processors commonly used in British Columbia. Other distinguishing features besides the processor type include the method for measuring the logs, the mechanisms used to feed the log through the processor, the machine size, and the carrier type. These characteristics can influence the success of using a particular type of processor on a given site.

### Processor type
The market offers a variety of machines that are grouped here as "processors." These machines use different processing methods and generate different products, factors that should be considered before selecting the type of processor to use. The size and form of the timber are also important factors to consider. Stroke delimbers and dangle-head processors can delimb and produce measured logs. Stationary delimbers remove limbs but usually cannot cut the logs to length, while slashers only cut the logs to length. Debarkers and chippers complete the spectrum — they are used to produce chips for pulp mills.

***Stroke delimber***   Stroke delimbers have a sliding boom with a grapple at the end for picking up the logs and removing the branches. After the log is lifted from the pile, a second grapple mounted on the fixed portion of the boom holds the butt end of the log while the grip on the top-end grapple is relaxed. As the boom is extended out-wards, the sharp edges of the grapple arms cut off the branches. When the boom reaches the top of the tree, the saw or shear is activated to cut off the top. The butt portion of the log continues to be held in the grapples, and logs longer than a pre-ferred length are cut into shorter logs as the boom is

retracted. The tops and short logs fall away from the head into the log deck. Finally, the butt log is discharged into a pile, usually near the location where it was picked up originally.

For logs that are longer than the single-stroke capacity of the boom, stroke delimbers can pull the log back through the machine by alternating the grip on the top-end and butt-end grapples while moving the boom. Very long logs can be processed by repeating the in-and-out action several times.

Some stroke delimbers incorporate powered rollers to feed the logs through the machine and reduce the amount of stroking required by the boom. Stroke delimbers are manufactured in both single-piece and telescopic boom models — the single-piece booms offer increased strength for larger timber, but their reach and speed is less compared with telescopic-boom models.

Stroke delimbers usually have a second saw on the fixed portion of the boom for trimming the butt-end of the logs. Trimming is done before starting the delimbing function

**Figure 95**
*A stroke delimber working on a landing. The butt end of this large log can be seen protruding from the end of the tunnel on the left.*

so that the length-measuring system can start measuring from a known point. The various options for measuring systems are discussed later.

When working in roadside systems, strokers travel on the road surface and work on logs piled immediately adjacent to the road. Strokers work equally well from landings, processing logs from piles or from single logs as they are dropped by the skidders. The range of vertical movement of the boom limits the maximum sideslope where stroke delimbers can work successfully. About 20% immediately adjacent to the road is the maximum sideslope for successful roadside operations. Similarly, the maximum boom elevation limits the maximum height for piling logs.

Although typically built on standard excavator carriers, stroke delimbers are purpose-built machines that are dedicated solely to processing.

### OPERATIONAL

Since strokers deposit processed logs close to their original location, they are well suited to roadside processing. Skidders can drop the logs at the road's edge, and the processor can work from the road surface. The typical procedure is to travel along the pile of

**Figure 96**
*The stroke delimber continues to hold the butt end of the log after cutting off the top. Several trees can be cut simultaneously.*

logs, with the whole trees on one side of the processor, a working area in the middle, and the processed logs on the other side. The machine typically swings only 20–30 degrees during the normal operating cycle, making it highly productive.

Sorting the logs is usually accomplished by staggering the butts at various distances from the road's edge, or by piling one sort on top of another with an obvious angle between the two sorts. Two or three sorts can be accommodated quite easily. For additional sorts, logs can be piled in the ditchline, on the road surface, or on the opposite side of the road.

Stroke delimbers require two passes over each log, providing both a cost and a benefit. Two strokes over the log require more time than one stroke (as with dangle-head processors), which can become a significant factor for small logs. However, two strokes also provide the opportunity to measure the log before cutting. With sophisticated computerized measuring systems, this provides the opportunity to optimize the bucking decision based on the actual log measurements.

The maximum log size limit for strokers is determined by the tunnel diameter through the machine — the butt of every log must fit into the tunnel. Stroke delimbers are typically more robust than dangle-head processors, and can handle larger limbs, such as those found on hardwood stems, more easily.

Because of these features, strokers are used more often for larger timber than dangle-head processors. Larger stroke delimbers can accept logs to about 70 cm diameter. Strokers are less efficient than dangle-head processors for timber under 30 cm butt diameter.

Stroke delimbers operate from the road surface; therefore, they do not cause soil compaction adjacent to the road. Furthermore, the skidders travel all the way to the road before dropping their load of logs, and they turn around on the road surface. The amount of traffic immediately adjacent to the road is reduced compared with dangle-head processors.

Furthermore, material that is trimmed from the logs' butts falls to the ground near the road surface, and may end up in the ditches. Post-harvesting cleanup must include clearing the ditches of this debris. The branches and tops are spread over a tree-length strip out from the road.

**Dangle-head processor**    Dangle-head processors consist of a processing head mounted at the end of the boom, often mounted on an excavator-style carrier. The processing head includes grapple arms, delimbing knives, a cutoff saw, and a drive system for moving the logs through the processor. The various drive systems are discussed later.

In the typical cycle, the processor lifts a tree from the pile and trims the butt if required. Then it swings towards the output pile while engaging the head's drive system, causing the tree to move through the head and the delimbing knives to cut off the limbs. Long trees are cut immediately into measured logs as the head reaches the correct length.

**Figure 97**
*A dangle-head processor working at roadside in a typical, small-diameter stand appropriate for this type of equipment.*

Upon reaching the top of the tree, the cutoff saw is engaged to make the final cut. As the carrier swings back towards the input pile, it discards the top into a debris pile. Unlike stroke delimbers, dangle-head processors move the logs lengthwise from one location to another during processing.

The carrier can be used for other types of operations by replacing the dangle-head processor with other tools.

Feller-processors are similar to dangle-head processors, and are sometimes used only for processing. However, they may have difficulty grasping trees from a log deck because the grab arms are designed to grasp standing trees. Feller-processor heads are discussed in more detail in the section on mechanized felling equipment.

Dangle-head processors are inherently faster than stroke delimbers because they make just one pass over the log. Although important when processing small timber, this advantage tends to be lost as the tree size increases because the trees are not moved as easily. For large trees that cannot be held in the processor, they can be rested on the ground and the processor passed over them by swinging the carrier.

The single-pass mode of operation has implications with regard to log-size optimization because the processor must cut the logs before the full length of the tree has been measured. In contrast, stroke delimbers measure the entire tree before cutting the logs. Therefore, optimizing functions on dangle-head processors will tend to be less precise than stroke delimbers because they are based on estimates of the tree profile. However, the single-pass mode is not an issue if the cutting decision is based on length or diameter, instead of the tree profile.

Together, these factors mean that dangle-head processors are better suited to smaller timber than to larger timber. Trees in the 20–40 cm butt diameter class are ideally suited to processing with typical dangle-head processors.

Depending on the configuration of the grapple arms and drive system, dangle-head processors may have some difficulty picking up logs from a pile. Some designs have drive-wheels on the arms, which make them bulky and awkward to pick up the logs. Generally, dangle-head processors pick up logs more easily from loosely packed piles.

Dangle-head processors are better suited than stroke delimbers for cutting multiple short logs from a tree because of the different ways the trees are held and cut. With dangle-head processors, the log is cut from the butt and the remainder of the tree is held in the head, ready to continue processing. With strokers, by contrast, the top part falls away, and the butt portion is held in the grapples. Since bucking should proceed from the butt end of the tree, the first log has to be discharged and the top picked up again before a second log can be cut.

Sorting the logs into more than two piles is more difficult with dangle-head processors than strokers because of the way they hold the trees. The trees in the input pile should line up with the logs in the output deck, and variation of log position within the deck is limited. Stroke delimbers, on the other hand, can vary the angle of the logs more easily. Therefore, dangle-head processors are less suitable to operations where multiple sorts are required.

**ENVIRONMENTAL**

Dangle-head processors require a different skidding layout for roadside processing than stroke delimbers. The trees must be dropped by the skidders about one log-length away from the road edge — processing the logs takes them the final distance up to the road edge. This means that skidder traffic for turning around and aligning the butts occurs off the road surface, in contrast to stroke delimbers where this traffic occurs on the road surface. The extra traffic may lead to increased soil compaction on the area adjacent to the road.

### Pull-through stationary delimbers

These delimbers work with another machine in either the cutblock landing or a central sortyard. The auxiliary machine, which can be a skidder or hydraulic loader, pulls the trees past a set of delimbing knives to remove the limbs. The delimber may also include a saw for topping the trees. Without a topping saw, another method such as a hand-bucker must be provided to cut off the tree tops.

When used with a measuring rack and cutoff saw, these systems can also cut the trees to length. The measuring racks are configured with one or more fixed-length gaps, and the loader simply butts the trees against a stop-plate to measure the correct log lengths. Both machines are operated by remote control by the loader operator, either via radio or direct cable hookup.

The benefit of these delimbers is their low capital cost compared with dangle-head processors and stroke delimbers, and their low labour cost compared with hand-buckers. The low cost makes these delimbers suitable for low-production operations.

**Figure 98**
*This simple, pull-through delimber uses the weight of the logs to close the delimber arms — no power or remote control is required. The loader simply pulls the logs through the delimbing arms. The tines on the bottom of the delimber work themselves into the ground to prevent the delimber from slipping*

## Other processors

The following processors are not commonly used in British Columbia, being limited to specialized applications. As environmental regulations make it increasingly difficult to host large, industrial operations anywhere but a centralized sortyard, their usage within cutblocks is becoming even more rare. Centralized operations eliminate rehabilitation work on the landings and create economies of scale by servicing a wider area from a single location.

*Chippers* Chippers can be used for chip production from raw logs or from salvage and debris cleanup. The choice between these functions is partially determined by high-level forest policy. The sawmills in British Columbia can produce lumber from the smallest trees; therefore, the primary goal is to maximize the amount of sawlogs delivered to the mills. Consequently, chippers are used mainly for cleanup or salvage operations. However, the primary use of the small trees in other jurisdictions is for pulp chips, so in-woods or "satellite" chipping operations are more common.

**Figure 99**
*This mobile drum chipper was used to convert roadside and landing debris into pulp chips.*

Transportation costs can be reduced by sorting the raw logs closer to their source, then producing chips and shipping only usable mate-

**Figure 100**
*A large, integrated chipper, debarker, and delimber operating at roadside. This chipper was operating outside British Columbia.*

rial to the mills. This strategy is especially important where the fibre source is highly decadent.

There are two types of chippers — disc and drum. The main differences between them include the amount of energy consumed to produce chips and their ability to produce chips of uniform size and shape from different size logs. Disc chippers require less energy because of the kinetic energy stored in the quickly spinning disc. They can also produce more uniform chips than drum chippers from larger-diameter logs, but they do not perform as well for short pieces. Disc chippers are preferred for long logs, while drums are preferred for cleanup operations.

Chippers can be integrated or stand-alone machines. The integrated models incorporate the functions of delimbers, debarkers, and chippers, while the stand-alone machines are used with separate delimbing and debarking machines, or with screens for removing the debris after chipping.

Trucking is an important component of the chipping operation because a chip van must always be present for the chipper to operate. Without a chip van on-site, the chipper must stop production or store the chips in a temporary location such as a surge bin.

***Chain-flail delimbers*** Chain-flail delimbers can be stand-alone machines, or integrated into chippers. Chain-flail delimbers remove the branches from trees by means of chains fastened to one or more rotating drums. The branches are literally beaten off the stems by the force of the flailing chains. The chain-flail has two variations — the stationary version which pulls the trees through a chamber that encloses the drum, and a mobile version which is carried by a wheeled loader. The loader drives over the trees to perform the delimbing.

**Figure 101**
*A mobile chain-flail delimber.*

These machines were originally developed as a method for delimbing small trees. However, chain flails cannot cut the tops off the trees, so additional processing is still required after they have completed their work. Because of this limitation, chain flails are seldom used except as part of an integrated delimber-debarker-chipper machine.

***Debarkers, hoggers*** Separate debarkers are required for chipper installations that do not use multi-function chippers. Chain-flail debarkers are similar to delimbers, but they are purpose-built, and have more aggressive settings for removing bark. Other debarkers resemble the machines used at sawmills (i.e., ring, drum, or cradle debarkers). These machines are large and heavy, and are usually seen as part of a semi-permanent installation.

**Figure 102**
*A cradle-type debarker used in a satellite processing yard. The cradle contains rotating serrated discs, and is slanted towards one end. The logs are tumbled inside the cradle until they emerge, debarked, from the low end of the cradle.*

Hoggers are used to grind waste material into a mixture that can be used for fuel in various power-generation plants. Hog fuel derived from sortyard waste has also been used as a carbon source in composting operations. Sortyard debris is a candidate for hog-fuel production, but experiments have also shown that landing or roadside debris from logging operations can also be converted into hog fuel.

**Figure 103**
*This machine produced hog fuel as part of a debris-management program at a coastal sortyard. The hog fuel was used as an energy source at a nearby pulp mill.*

***Slashers*** Slashers are used to cut trees into short logs, usually several trees at a time. These machines are common in eastern Canada where the more extensive infrastructure can deliver short logs to the mills. However, slashers have been used in western Canada for processing hardwood bolts. Slashers are appropriate where the requirements are for a high volume of a uniform product with little sorting.

***"Tray-based" processors*** Processors that feed the logs through a central "tray" in a stationary chassis have been labelled "tray-based" for this handbook. With features of both slashers and stroke delimbers, these machines can delimb, top, and measure logs. They have only a limited ability to sort the logs, and require an auxiliary machine to bring the trees to the processing site and remove the manufactured logs. The logs are fed longitudinally through the machine, so it must be parked crossways on the road when used in a cutblock. This feature limits their usefulness to central sortyards with ample room to maneuver the logs.

## Log-measurement methods

Sawmills usually require the logs to be measured and cut to preferred lengths before delivery, and minor length variations are significant — 5 cm is a typical allowance for under-length logs. Many lumber products are sold in 60-cm increments rather than random lengths, and logs that are cut too short for one length will result in wastage as the boards are cut to the next-shorter length. Log lengths for panel-board plants are even more critical because shorter panels are completely unacceptable. Also, provincial regulations limit the overall length for trucks travelling on public highways, so the logs must be cut to lengths that are legal to haul on public roads.

The length-measurement system must be indexed to the end of the tree before measurement starts. Photocells that sense the end of the tree are commonly used, and they must be kept clear of debris to function properly. Photocells are sometimes fooled by bright sunshine. Some stroke delimbers use a butt-plate over the tunnel as a fixed measuring point. These systems are foolproof providing the log is butted against the plate, but work well only for short logs because the butt-plate must be moved away from the tunnel for long logs.

Feller-processors can be used for processing only, but may not be optimal for that task because they are designed to grasp standing trees. Feller-processors often use the chainsaw blade as the zero-point — they presume that the chainsaw is positioned at the end of the tree immediately after falling. If the feller-processor is used for processing trees out of a pile, then an extra step is required to index the saw blade to the end of the tree.

All log-measuring devices rely on sensors and encoders to translate various physical measurements into estimates of the log length. Many dangle-head processors use spiked wheels that roll along the logs. These systems work well when kept clean and in proper contact with the logs. However, bark, snow, and ice can accumulate in the spikes to cause slippage and incorrect measurements. Errors can also be introduced if the encoder wheel bounces over knots or limbs. Other dangle-head processors use encoders on the drive system; these types are subject to errors when the drive wheels slip, such as when encountering an oversized limb.

Stroke delimbers typically use encoders that measure the extension of the boom, and translate the boom position into the log length. These encoders are less susceptible to slippage than encoders that ride on the log, but they also require an accumulating function for when the tree is stroked back and forth in the machine. If the tree slips in the grapples, then measurement errors will be introduced.

Regardless of the underlying technology used to derive the log length, the best precision for any system will occur when the system is checked and calibrated regularly.

Fixed-length measuring systems such as those used by slashers and measuring racks result in the most reliable length measuring, but they are limited to the number of log lengths that can be measured. When only one or two lengths are required, then these systems may be adequate.

Most processors can measure the minimum top diameter, and some processors can measure the log diameters continuously. Integrating length and diameter measurement with a computer results in log-profile measurements, a rare feature in the processors used in British Columbia.

Diameter-measurement systems can be more or less complex than the length-measurement systems. Knowing the diameter at any point along the log is difficult to obtain accurately — variations or inaccuracies in log-diameter measurements are caused by surface defects, non-circular cross-sections, and variations in bark thickness along the stem. In practice, continuous diameter measurement is required only if the processor is configured to buck according to log-value tables that are based on diameters. On the other hand, knowing that the log's top diameter is not less than the minimum acceptable diameter is important information. Such information can be obtained with a simple limit-switch on the grapple arms to signal when the arms have closed beyond a certain point. This type of measurement can be obtained easily from either stroke delimbers or dangle-head processors.

### Feeding mechanisms
Dangle-head processors and some stroke delimbers drive the tree through the head to perform the delimbing action. This requires that the machine grips the tree with some mechanism to move it. Also, the type of drive mechanism can affect log quality and length-measurement accuracy.

The drive mechanisms can be broken into two groups: wheels or tracks. Wheels are more compact and of simpler construction, but their contact area with the log is limited. On the other hand, tracks have more contact area, and thus have less slippage on the tree, but they are bulkier and more complex.

Various wheel modifications are used to reduce the slippage. These modifications, which include adding spikes, ribs, or knobs to the wheels to increase their grip, can also increase the risk of damaging the outermost fibres on the logs. Since the highest-value boards are cut from the outside of the logs, spike-roller damage to the logs can be significant, and should be avoided for sawlogs. However, spike-roller damage is inconsequential if the trees are used only for pulp. Scandinavian equipment commonly uses rubber tires instead of steel wheels to provide a softer grip to the logs, thus reducing damage to the logs. However, the rubber wheels have less grip on the logs, which can impair the ability to remove large limbs, and may reduce the maximum feed speed. Rubber tires are usually fitted with tire chains to improve traction.

Some dangle-head processors have drive mechanisms that engage only the top of the log, while others have drive wheels on the grapple arms so the log can be driven from three sides. The multi-side approach improves traction, and the ability to remove larger limbs without slippage, but it also makes the grapple arms bulkier, and makes it more difficult to penetrate the log deck to pick up the logs.

**Figure 104**
*A single-grip feller-processor head showing the feed rollers on movable arms. The encoding wheel for length measurement and the third drive wheel are located in the centre of the machine.*

## Size

The operating conditions for processors are generally less variable than the conditions for other phases. For processing, the primary determining factors are tree size and limb size, not terrain and soil conditions. Consequently, the decision is often whether to use mechanical processing at all, not to select the proper size of processor; or, a decision may be required regarding the type of processor. As discussed previously, dangle-head processors work better for small trees than stroke delimbers, and vice versa for larger trees.

Where processor size is an issue, the processor must be able to handle most trees over the long term without experiencing mechanical failure or unacceptable costs. Occasionally, large trees can be processed manually, and too many small trees with a large processor will increase processing costs. Manufacturers offer a range of sizes for some processors, but the range is generally limited compared with the equipment for other phases.

In some hardwood stands, the average tree size may not be large, but the trees may have large-diameter limbs. Further, hardwood limbs are generally regarded as difficult to remove and hard on equipment. A large, robust delimber is required for these conditions. As an alternative, some companies use hand-buckers to cut the tops off the trees to reduce the wear and tear on the processors.

## Carrier

Most processors used in British Columbia are mounted on excavator carriers, although a few are rubber-tire mounted. Rubber tires allows for quick moves between work sites, an advantage for small cutblocks that are located within a few kilometres of each other. Tracked machines would require a low-bed over the same distances. However, tracked machines provide a more stable work platform, either on the road or at the stump.

## LOADING EQUIPMENT

Earlier in the forest industry's development in British Columbia, rail, flume, water, and animal transportation systems were used to transport logs. These methods have now largely disappeared in favour of trucking. Some operations do not use trucks (e.g., helicopters flying directly to water drops), but mostly, the final phase of harvesting is to load the logs onto a truck using a loader.

Loaders fall into two categories: front-end loaders, which travel between the log pile and the truck while loading, and swing loaders, which remain more-or-less in one location while loading. Swing loaders include both hydraulic loaders and line loaders. The amount of space required for efficient operation differs significantly between these two types of loader, and is the primary factor for choosing the type of loader. The loader's maximum reaching distance and height and the ability to reach below grade are also important. Other distinguishing characteristics are the carrier type and the size.

### Common Features of Loading Equipment

Although the task for loaders seems simple — put the logs onto the trucks — it can be complex. They must load the trucks for maximum payload within the legal limits and sort the logs or keep previously sorted logs separated during loading. The loads must also be safe (i.e., balanced side-to-side with no loose or protruding logs that would pose a safety hazard to other traffic). The logs should not be damaged, their ends should be aligned as required, and the operating cost should be minimized.

Often, the ratio of butt-ahead and butt-back logs on the truck must be balanced to maximize payload. With swing loaders, the logs are simply turned end-for-end as they are being loaded, but front-end loaders cannot accomplish this task as easily. The logs must be turned end-for-end away from the truck before approaching it for loading. Turning the log involves setting it on the ground, and driving to the other side before picking it up again. Alternatively, large landings are required so that the truck can be parked in the middle of the landing, allowing the loader to work from both sides.

Sorting logs requires room to store the various grades in separate piles before they are loaded onto the trucks. Safe loads are built tightly, with long logs on the outside, and shorter logs inside. All safety regulations must be observed.

The common feature is that larger landings usually permit loaders to work more efficiently.

Efficiency for loading is usually maximized when the loading is separated from the extraction and processing phases. However, the loader cannot be separated from the truck fleet, and scheduling the log trucks for maximum efficiency can often create conflicts. Ideally, the loader will work continuously, never having to wait for trucks. But if too many trucks are assigned to the loader, they will be forced to wait. Having more than one loader in an operating area can help with scheduling; however, this setup may be difficult to achieve with independent logging contractors and is more feasible with single-company operations.

# Distinguishing Features of Loading Equipment

## Machine mobility

As a rule of thumb, front-end loaders are used on flatter terrain where large landings can be built relatively easily, while swing loaders are used on steeper terrain where small landings are more common.

***Front-end loaders*** Front-end loaders, both tracked and wheeled, require a significant amount of space for operating. They load the log truck from the side, and need enough room to turn between the truck and the log deck. Consequently, front-end loaders work better for landing operations than roadside operations.

**Figure 105**
*A front-end loader operating from a landing in a cut-to-length operation.*

### OPERATIONAL

Front-end loaders are relatively easy to operate, partly because they grasp the logs firmly in large forks. This action provides the operator with positive control of the logs as compared with line loaders in which the logs have more freedom to move. Several logs can be picked up simultaneously for quicker loading.

Front-end loaders require flat ground for operating — any side-to-side motion caused by uneven ground is amplified in the logs as the machine travels over the ground.

Most front-end loaders are rubber-tired, so they are quick to move between operating areas. Low-bed transportation is not usually required unless significant distances (over 20 km) are involved.

### ENVIRONMENTAL

The amount of space required for sorting, storing, and loading logs means that front-end loaders typically need large landings. Furthermore, the large amount of traffic on the landings causes severe soil compaction, unsuitable for growing another crop of trees. Rehabilitation measures such as ripping and recontouring the land may be required.

***Swing loaders*** Swing loaders, which feature a rotating superstructure mounted on a rubber-tired or tracked carrier, remain more-or-less in one spot during loading. The logs are picked up in a grapple and swung around onto the truck, either from the end or from the side.

Swing loaders have two distinct classes — line or heelboom loaders and

**Figure 106**
*Line loaders are common in coastal operations. This loader is modified with a "super snorkel" to extend its reach to about 50 m from the centre of the road.*

hydraulic loaders. Line loaders are more typical in coastal operations, while hydraulic loaders are used throughout the province. Line loaders are typically larger than hydraulic loaders.

The grapple in a line loader is supported by two or three cables that are attached to drums on the winch. By reeling in or releasing the cables, the grapple can be opened or closed, raised or lowered. During operation, the logs are grappled off-centre such that the butt-end is higher than the top. The butt is pivoted, or "heeled," against the underside of the boom, which prevents the log from pivoting in the grapple.

Being attached to cables, the grapple can be "cast" 10–20 m to retrieve logs that are outside the loader's immediate reach. This capability is especially important on steep cutblocks where the logs can easily slide off the landing after unhooking.

Line loaders are difficult to operate, and require a lengthy training period for the operator to become proficient. Skilled line loader operators are highly valued.

Hydraulic loaders are easier to operate, accounting for their widespread use. Most hydraulic loaders pick up the logs lengthwise, similar to line loaders; the difference being that the grapple is attached firmly to the boom, instead of with cables. Hydraulic loaders are also easier to move, being mounted on excavator-style carriers. However, unlike line loaders, they are limited to grappling logs within their immediate reach. Hydraulic loaders are available in a wide variety of models and sizes.

A distinct style of hydraulic loader was developed for roadside logging. This type of loader, called the "butt 'n top" loader, grasps the logs in the middle, which facilitates loading from the side of the truck. Butt 'n top loaders can also turn the logs end-for-end

to equalize the payload between the truck and trailer. Outrigger arms on the grapple balance the logs.

**OPERATIONAL**

Cable yarding systems often require a swing loader. As the logs are unhooked from the chokers, the loader moves them to a temporary storage location where they can be bucked to length, and otherwise processed.

The sorting capacity for swing loaders is limited somewhat by the number of logs that can be piled in the area immediately adjacent to the loader. Furthermore, swing loaders tend to concentrate activity in one area — unhooking, processing, sorting, and loading all must occur close together. This congestion can lead to hazards and production inefficiencies, and makes swing loaders less favourable than front-end loaders with ground-based extraction on landings.

When these loaders work with cable yarders, breaks in yarding activity are commonly used to pick up timber from nearby areas. This practice can help to lower the overall costs by providing more consistent production. These loaders are also used as primary transport machines in their own right, either as loader-forwarders, cherry pickers, or super snorkels. These uses are discussed under ground-based extraction equipment, elsewhere in the handbook.

### ENVIRONMENTAL

Swing loaders can operate from smaller landings than front-end loaders of equivalent capacity. This feature is especially important in steep terrain where building large landings is difficult, expensive, and environmentally intrusive.

Line loaders are typically very heavy machines, and require a high road standard to support their weight. Hydraulic loaders are more mobile, and may be able to operate from less substantial road surfaces.

## Carrier

Both types of loaders (front-end and swing) are available on either rubber-tired carriers or tracked carriers. The intended use for the loader determines the choice of carriers.

*Wheeled*   Rubber-tired carriers are faster to move between work sites, but they also require better running surfaces than equivalent tracked machines. Wheeled loaders are used for various loading tasks, both in the Interior and the Coast, and are some of the most common machines in the logging industry.

**Figure 109**
*A rubber-mounted line loader. This type of carrier provides more mobility than tracked designs.*

Swing loaders, both line and hydraulic, can be mounted on rubber-tired carriers. These machines require retractable stabilizer pads to reduce the bouncing effect caused by the rubber tires. The stabilizers typically reach outside the machine's wheelbase, which must be accounted for in the road specifications. Steep, narrow roads are especially problematic for rubber-mounted line loaders because of their large size, height, and weight.

Rubber-tired carriers for small hydraulic loaders can be either factory-built or truck-mounted. Neither type is very common in British Columbia, and they are usually used only for specialized applications.

*Tracked*   Common at one time, tracked front-end loaders are seldom used in British Columbia anymore. These machines can work under more adverse soil conditions than wheeled loaders, but this ability is no longer an advantage because of the more stringent soil disturbance limits in place today. Tracked machines are also slower and more expensive to maintain than wheeled loaders.

Tracked carriers are the standard for swing loaders, both line and hydraulic, because they provide a more stable operating platform than rubber-tired carriers. Butt 'n top loaders that work in roadside operations must be track-mounted to travel over the unprepared surface adjacent to the road.

However, tracked carriers also incur higher costs as compared with wheeled carriers for travel between work sites, an important factor to consider with small cutblocks. Hydraulic loaders may be moved short distances under their own power, but line loaders are typically moved on a low-bed even for distances less than 1 km.

***Self-loading trucks*** Some trucks have an integral hydraulic loader for loading and unloading logs, independent of any other equipment. Self-loaders are usually smaller that stand-alone loaders, so their reaching and loading capacity is less, and the truck payload is reduced by the loader's weight. The boom design, which is different than typical hydraulic loaders, gives the operator less control over the log. As well, the operator is usually exposed to the weather.

**Figure 110**
*The self-loading log truck can operate anywhere the truck can drive. Self-loaders can pick up scattered loads without the expense of moving a loader.*

The advantage of self-loading trucks is that they can pick up loads from scattered locations and transport them to equally diverse locations without the extra costs of hiring and transporting a loader.

Some self-loading trucks are especially configured for shortwood operations, with a truck and full trailer. The loader is mounted at the rear of the truck so it can reach both the truck and trailer sections.

The self-loading truck is indispensable for specialized operations where the production is scattered among several small piles in various locations (e.g., thinning). Self-loading trucks are usually associated with low-volume or cleanup operations, although some companies use self-loaders as their primary truck fleet.

## Size

Because the equipment size governs the maximum lifting weight, the loaders operating on the Coast are often large to lift the large, old-growth logs. However, the loader must also lift the trailer off the log truck in preparation for loading. In many cases, the trailer is the heaviest load for the loader to lift, and the loader must be sized accordingly.

Size also affects the reaching distance and the cost. Reaching distance is especially important on steep terrain, where the loader may be required to grapple a log that has slid off the landing. If the log is beyond the loader's reach, then rehooking it with the yarder may be required. Cherry pickers are large to maximize the amount of timber that can be reached from the road.

Lastly, size determines the loader's agility. Small loaders can operate within partial cuts without damaging the residual crop. When working with a yarder, the loader must not rub against the guylines — large loaders may cause an accident if they were to catch one of the guylines.

# OPERATING TECHNIQUES

As described previously, each machine type is defined by some basic features that make it suitable for a range of site conditions. Conversely, few sites are suited to just one type of equipment — often changing the operating methods will make the difference between the success and failure of using a particular equipment type.

This section will describe various operating techniques, and their effects on operational and environmental considerations. While the emphasis is on primary transport equipment, the other phases will also be mentioned.

## Ground-based Primary Transport

### Roadside versus landing systems

One distinguishing characteristic between harvesting systems is whether the logs are transported to roadside or landing. This decision has major implications on harvesting economics plus some impacts on the post-harvesting activities.

OPERATIONAL

One technique to reduce logging costs is to ensure that each machine is used as much as possible on every shift. Separating the phases with stockpiles of logs is one way to achieve this goal because a delay in one phase will have minimal impact on previous or subsequent phases. The key to roadside logging is to allow adequate

**Figure 111**
*The flat slope in this cutblock allows the skidder to drop the logs at any location along the road's length.*

space to stockpile the logs — a rule of thumb in the Interior is to separate each phase by about one week's production.

Roadside logging often implies full-tree or tree-length skidding with grapples or clambunks, but cut-to-length, horse logging, loader-forwarders, and cherry pickers are also used in roadside systems. It is also used where full trees are skidded to roadside and trucked to a central location for processing. For this section, "roadside logging" will refer to the narrow definition of full-tree or tree-length systems using skidders or clambunks, with subsequent mechanical processing.

A primary consideration for roadside logging is the sideslope adjacent to the roads. The sideslopes must be less than 15–20% to stockpile and process the logs because the processors have difficulty reaching the logs on steeper ground. The

**Figure 112**
*A clambunk skidder piling logs at the roadside by offloading with its grapple.*

entire road does not need to be suitable for processing logs, but a rule of thumb is that at least one-third of the road's length must be suitable. The ground itself must be free of large obstacles that would prevent stockpiling the logs or impede travel for the loader.

Roadside operations allow a great deal of flexibility to combine various machines into systems such that each machine works optimally. Even though the individual machines may work at different rates, they can be combined in different numbers, shift lengths, or number of shifts per day to ensure that each machine is fully utilized. Roadside logging also eliminates the congestion that occurs in landings and can improve the safety environment for workers.

The high degree of mechanization required for roadside logging results in very high capital costs, which subsequently requires a large harvesting volume to amortize the equipment costs at an economical rate. Roadside logging can achieve low unit costs, but only when based on high productivity.

Hand-bucking of small trees of roadside decks is generally impractical because of safety, logistical, and productivity concerns; therefore, mechanical processing is required. Productivity for mechanical processing is highest when all the trees are oriented with their butts in the same direction; therefore, mechanized falling is usually used with roadside logging.

The processor type influences its practicality for roadside processing. Stroke delimbers return the processed logs to about the same location where they were retrieved, but dangle-head processors move the logs from one location to another during processing. This design feature means that the logs must be decked about one log-length away from the road edge, with the logs becoming aligned with the road edge only after processing. Because of this design difference, stroke delimbers are more commonly used for roadside processing than dangle-head processors.

Because the loader must be able to operate from an unprepared surface, wheeled front-end loaders are unsuitable for roadside systems. Furthermore, optimizing trucking costs under typical highway weight restrictions requires that some of the butts be aligned to the front of the truck while the remainder be aligned to the rear of the truck. Since the logs are all aligned in one direction after processing, a butt 'n top loader is required to alternate the log orientation.

However, roadside logging is impractical for some locations. The sideslope adjacent to the roads may be too steep — if not enough space is available on suitable terrain to deck the timber for processing, "hot processing and loading" is required. The timber may be too large for mechanical processing or other resource constraints may require the use

**Figure 113**

*Small landings can become congested with equipment and logs.*

of less-mechanized systems. Every operating division will have some volume that must be logged to landings, and the licensee must decide how best to accommodate this requirement for flexibility. Two different methods are (1) to ensure that each contractor has the equipment required for all conditions, or (2) to employ a range of contractors specialized for different conditions. Each method has its benefits, and the outcome of this decision will vary among licensees depending on their corporate requirements.

Landing-based operations are typically less mechanized than roadside operations. Therefore, landing-based operations are more appropriate when more log manufacturing is required or in niche operations such as cleanup around riparian areas. The volume of timber may be insufficient to justify the transportation costs for a large, mechanized operation, and less-mechanized equipment may be more appropriate. Landings are usually required for steeper ground where the highly mechanized equipment cannot operate.

**Figure 114**
*A line skidder pulls a turn into a landing as the front-end loader waits for the next truck to arrive.*

Many landings are restricted to less than 0.3 ha. With this landing size, the amount of log storage space is limited, and all phases must work more closely together on either one or several landings. Two or three concurrent landings in an operating area can help optimize productivity, but even with multiple landings, the travel time between landings can make it impractical to separate the phases. There is less opportunity to combine shifts of different lengths, or for the machines to work different numbers of shifts per day. As a result, the productivity of all machines is usually limited by the rate of the slowest phase.

### ENVIRONMENTAL

Roadside and landing systems have considerably different machine-travel patterns over the cutblock, which can influence whether the site's growth potential becomes degraded after harvesting. In roadside systems, the traffic is dispersed over a wider area. Almost every part of the cutblock receives some traffic, and the areas near the roadside undergo many cycles of machine traffic. The first one to five passes may cause the greatest portion of the total compaction, so the entire cutblock could be affected. However, the impact of machine traffic depends largely on the site characteristics and operating conditions, and even many passes may result in no compaction under some conditions. In contrast, the traffic in landing-based systems is concentrated on fewer skid trails, especially near the landings. Trails may become severely compacted and require subsequent site rehabilitation, but the extent of the impact is well defined. Note that the choice between roadside and landing systems can influence the amount and extent of site disturbance.

See the following "Skidding pattern" discussion and the "Site and Stand Characteristics" section later in the handbook for additional information about skidding patterns and soil impacts.

The limbs and tops that accumulate during mechanical processing could reduce the amount of plantable area for some sites; the debris is commonly piled on the road for subsequent burning. Excavators are increasingly used for roadside cleanup because of their lower soil disturbance as compared with crawler tractors. Debris from landings must be piled and burned (if permitted), and fire guards may be required around the landing.

More care must be taken with roadside harvesting to restore all drainage structures properly after operations are completed because they could become plugged with logging debris.

After dropping the logs at roadside, the usual practice is to push them into a pile with the skidder, which increases the amount of machine traffic immediately adjacent to the road and potentially increases the amount of soil compaction and log breakage. An alternative is simply to drop the logs at the roadside and to pile them with a log loader.

**Figure 115**
*The skidders dropped the logs at the roadside, and the loader moved them into piles, which reduced the amount of roadside traffic.*

This method may result in less ground compaction, but with additional costs. However, the contractor that FERIC observed using this technique said that increased productivity for the skidders offset the loader cost.

The silvicultural system has an influence on the choice between roadside or landing operations. Landings are usually used in partial cutting systems to provide for loading sites where machine operations will not damage the residual stand. In roadside operations, sufficient trees must be removed to provide a clear working area.

### Skidding pattern

As defined for this handbook, three skidding patterns are commonly used in British Columbia: random skidding, designated trails, and return trails. Random skidding is typical for gentle terrain where topography does not limit machine travel, and traffic is not concentrated at any specific location. With designated trails, the travel routes are predetermined and usually marked in the field. The skidders may travel entirely on the designated trails, or they may be used for a portion of the travel route. Designated trails are appropriate for steep or sensitive areas such as near gullies. On sites with sensitive soils, designated trails limit the areas where machines are allowed to travel, and thus limit the extent of soil disturbance. With return trails, the skidder travels on different routes for the outbound and inbound portions of the cycle.

OPERATIONAL

On gentle terrain, ground-based equipment can travel anywhere on the cutblock in a random pattern. As the terrain becomes steeper, bladed skid trails may be required for safe access. Generally, sideslopes of about 35% are considered to be the upper limit at which wheeled skidders can work safely off the trail.

With more emphasis on soil conservation and with the implementation of soil disturbance guidelines, constructing an extensive network of skid trails to accommodate skidders is less common to minimize soil disturbance. Instead, cable yarding is used more often, or operations are scheduled for winter on snow, when skid trails require less soil excavation.

Skid trails are used to reduce the risk of overturning the skidder, to allow faster travel, or to control the distribution of traffic. Costs are incurred to locate, construct, and rehabilitate trails after harvesting. On steep ground, skidders may be confined to the trails, which decreases productivity because the skidder operator must pull the chokers from the trail to the hookup site for the logs.

The return-trail pattern is used to avoid turning the skidders around on steep ground, thus reducing the risk of overturning the machine. The skidders use a trail constructed to the top of the hill on the outbound portion of the cycle. From the top, the skidders travel straight down the hill, picking up a turn of logs on the way. Intermediate trails may be built between the top and bottom of the cutblock to serve as both inbound and outbound trails depending on the skidding location relative to the trail.

### ENVIRONMENTAL

**Figure 116**
*High-density skid trails on steep terrain were once common, but this access pattern is no longer considered acceptable. Alternatives to this skidding pattern include designated skid trails or cable yarding.*

**Figure 117**
*A form of return-trail system. Parallel skid trails were located about five tree-lengths apart, and the skidder travelled straight downhill between trails to pick up the logs.*

Trails limit the extent of machine traffic, thus limiting the distribution of soil disturbance over the cutblock. However, the type of concentrated disturbance resulting from trail construction and use may be more detrimental than disturbance from random skidding.

Trails can become channels to concentrate surface water and cause soil erosion, or they can be compacted and reduce seedling growth. Careful layout and rehabilitation are required to maintain proper drainage patterns.

Random skidding and designated trails may be combined within a single cutblock, (e.g., portions of a cutblock may be steep enough to require trails while other portions are less steep). Skidders tend to gravitate towards a common trail around landings, but without designated trails, several routes may be used before a single trail becomes the preferred route. By designating a preferred route, the total amount of disturbed land area can be reduced around the landing.

With the return-trail system, the amount of soil disturbance may vary depending on the slope position. Soil disturbance will be less at the top of the slope where there is little traffic off the trails, but higher at the bottom where the traffic is more concentrated.

Clambunks work in a series of trails perpendicular to the haul road, accumulating a load as they travel back to the road; they may pass over each portion of land just one time. Forwarders follow the trail of the feller-processor, travelling on a mat of debris. With loader-forwarders, planning the travel routes can reduce soil disturbance by avoiding sensitive zones such as wet or soft ground. Where soft ground cannot be avoided, mats or debris placed on the trails must be used to spread the load and reduce soildisturbance. The trail should maximize the use of benches on steep ground, and careful planning is required to ensure that the machine can reach all the timber without leaving the trail.

## Operating period

To maximize the amount of timber harvested with each machine, some operations work two or more shifts per day, while others are limited to daytime operations only.

**OPERATIONAL**

Highly mechanized operations, where all workers are enclosed in machine cabs, can be conducted at night as well as during the day. This approach increases the total number

**Figure 118**
*Mechanical harvesting equipment with proper lighting allows for round-the-clock operations.*

of hours worked per year, which helps to amortize the capital cost of the machinery and reduce overall operating costs. Nighttime operations are typical for northern Interior locations where most of the annual harvest must be done in winter when the daylight period is short.

However, productivity at night is usually lower than during the day, given the same operating conditions, because of reduced visibility. Scheduling the more difficult areas for daylight operations can help maximize total productivity. Nighttime operations can also make maintenance more difficult — the machine operates in the evening when it might normally be serviced or repaired.

Some safety hazards or log-quality factors may be less visible at night than during daytime. Operating at night with on-the-ground workers is not feasible because of the safety hazard of working in the dark.

**ENVIRONMENTAL**

Boundary markings are less visible at night than during the day, and the risk of inadvertently crossing a boundary is higher. This risk increases near areas that are marked with several boundaries, such as machine-free zones near riparian management areas. Coordinating the day and night shifts so that operations along the boundary are done during the day and in the cutblock interior at night can minimize the risk of trespass into a sensitive zone. Reflective tape and paint on boundary lines can also help with nighttime visibility.

## Method of trail construction

Three types of machines can be used to construct trails: skidders, crawler tractors, or excavators.

**OPERATIONAL**

Because wheeled skidders can construct only the simplest trails — they can only clear logs out of the way and do minor excavation — a machine capable of making a soil cut is required for building trails on steep ground. The crawler tractor was used most often in the past, but recently the hydraulic excavator has been become more common for constructing trails.

Since trailbuilding is not a full-time job, the trailbuilder must either be used for other purposes or sit idle for part of the time. Many contractors have old tractors used for miscellaneous purposes, such as building trails. One worker may do this job as a part-time activity, or the tractor may be used for skidding as required. Kockx and Krag (1993) found that the experience and skill of the operator played a large role in the site disturbance caused by trailbuilders. They also found that the trailbuilder and skidders must be matched closely in size, and that switching to a smaller trailbuilder did not necessarily result in smaller trails unless the skidders are also downsized.

Excavators equipped with buckets can be used very successfully for trailbuilding; with quick-change attachments they can also be used for site preparation, cleanup, or loader-forwarding.

In winter, a tractor may be required to clear the snow for the wheeled skidders.

## ENVIRONMENTAL

Excavators can keep topsoil and subsoil separated during construction and have more control over placement of the soil to facilitate easier and more effective rehabilitation after harvesting. Excavators can also work in more sensitive areas such as near streams because they do not cause as much soil disturbance when turning. They can be used to construct temporary crossings or to place portable bridges without encroaching on the stream.

## Protection of the residual stand

Protection of the residual stand refers to preserving advance regeneration as the overstorey is removed, or avoiding damage to the remaining trees in a partial cutting silvicultural system. This protection must not only be considered at the extraction phase, but also during planning, falling, and post-harvesting. Planning the patterns for cutting and extraction, and following the plans through completion, are the keys to successful protection of the residual stand.

**Figure 119**
*The shorter logs carried on forwarders are easier to maneuver between the residual trees in a partial cut than the full-length trees moved by skidders.*

## OPERATIONAL

The area travelled over by the harvesting equipment must be minimized; therefore, the falling and skidding equipment should use the same trails to minimize damage to the residual trees. Zero-swing feller-bunchers can work successfully from trails barely wider than their track widths, such as in partial cutting systems.

Cut-to-length systems using feller-processors have different capabilities and requirements than full-tree harvesting systems using feller-bunchers and skidders. Feller-processors cannot hold the trees vertically after they are cut from the stump, whereas feller-bunchers can keep the tree vertical. With feller-processors, the trees fall into the residual stand and may cause some damage. After falling, the trees are cut into short lengths and loaded onto forwarders.

**Figure 120**

*Rub trees prevent damage to the residual trees.*

The CTL system is well suited to protecting the residual crop because of the shorter logs. In full-tree or tree-length systems, the trails must be fairly straight to avoid the sweeping effect of dragging long logs behind a skidder. Where curves are required, leaving rub trees or posts will protect the crop trees and define the location of the skid trails. The rub trees can be felled manually and skidded after all the other trees have been harvested. The trails in CTL systems can have more curves, although very sharp corners will still cause problems with tree rubbing.

The trees must be felled in the proper orientation towards the trail. Feller-bunchers can hold the trees vertically after cutting, so they can be placed in the desired location and orientation. By working from the back of the trail, the feller-buncher can lay the trees on the trail, ready for the skidder. If this is not feasible, a "herringbone" pattern minimizes the turn angle for the trees to turn onto the trail.

**Figure 121**

*Falling the trees in a herringbone pattern with the butts facing the yarding corridors will help minimize damage to the residual trees.*

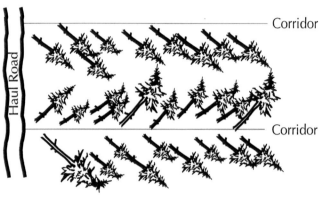

Operators of delimbers and other post-harvesting or support equipment must be instructed not to knock over residuals that have been protected during skidding.

**ENVIRONMENTAL**

In partial cutting systems, the fallers must ensure that the residual trees meet the proper requirements for species, size, form, and health. If the cutting prescription is complex, feller-buncher operators may be unable to distinguish properly between cut and leave trees, and tree marking or hand-falling may be required. With hand-falling, line skidders are also required to reach from the trails to the felled trees.

The root systems of the residual trees must be carefully protected. Increasing the stump heights will avoid having the skid plates on the felling head dig into the ground and sever the roots of the residuals.

Since many partial cutting systems require multiple entries into the stand over the rotation period, it is important to restrict machine traffic to the same skid trails during each entry to reduce the cumulative effects of soil disturbance.

# Cable Primary Transport

### Roadside versus landing

As with ground-based equipment, yarders can be used in roadside or landing operations, and many of the factors that apply to ground-based systems also apply to cable systems. The ability to separate the yarding and loading phases results in increased efficiency, and the safety aspects are improved because of decreased congestion around the landing. Refer to the discussion for ground-based operations for additional information.

#### OPERATIONAL

Roadside operations for cable systems are often limited to swing yarders because of their ability to pile the logs away from the immediate landing area.

**Figure 122 (L)**
*The terrain was too steep for decking off the road, and the swing capability of the yarder was required to land the logs on the road.*

**Figure 123 (R)**
*Small landings on steep hillsides often require that a yarder and loader work together to prevent logs from slipping down the embankment.*

Unlike ground-based systems, swing yarders can be used for roadside operations even on steep ground. Processing is usually done manually, and the sideslope must only be low enough to allow the logs to be decked without sliding back into the cutblock. About 60% is the maximum for piling logs with swing yarders configured for grapple yarding. For steeper areas, where the logs cannot be piled adjacent to the road, they can be piled on the road. Since a clear travel corridor out of the cutblock must be maintained at all times from the yarder, it must work from the back of the cutblock to the front. In turn, this requires that the full length of the road be yarded before loading commences to allow free access for the loader and trucks. Road layout that includes several spurs can help with scheduling the yarding and loading.

For yarding to landings, towers may be paired with an auxiliary machine, (e.g., a loader, skidder, or stroke delimber) to remove the logs after unhooking. In very steep locations, the loader may be required to hold the logs as they are unhooked, or the landing must provide a flat surface large enough to land the logs. However enlarging the landing may result in unacceptable or excessive soil disturbance and decrease the deflection for uphill yarding. Two-stage, "stepped" landings can help. Without a helper machine, the sideslope must also be low enough to unhook the logs safely without them sliding back into the cutblock. Various toothed devices that can be anchored to stumps can hold the logs safely while they are unhooked.

**Figure 124**
*Because of insufficient room to pile and load the logs near the tower, a skidder forwarded the logs to a landing.*

In addition to roadside and landing systems, cable yarders can also be used in "cold deck" systems in which the logs are yarded first to an intermediate location away from the truck road, and then yarded to the final destination over a second cable system. Cold decks were common in the early 1900s, when logging railways were located only in the valley bottoms, and cold decks provided access to steep areas where the railways could not be built. This system may be appropriate today for locations such as hanging valleys where road access is impossible.

### ENVIRONMENTAL

Even though there is no machine traffic to cause compaction on areas adjacent to the landing, soil disturbance may occur within the yarding roads themselves. Soil disturbance on the immediate roadside areas are less of a concern because the loading and processing phases typically occur on the road itself. However, the debris cleanup and water flow restoration issues are similar between the two systems. Being more typical of coastal areas where heavy precipitation is common, adequate drainage must be maintained at all times for cable-based roadside systems.

**Figure 125**
*The loader and stationary processor were located about 150 m from the tower.*

Large landings on steep ground can occupy a significant area. Landing size must be minimized, consistent with safe and economical operation. Proper drainage patterns must be maintained around landings to prevent surface water from being concentrated. Downhill yarding with towers tends to concentrate the water flow in the tracks left by the logs.

**Figure 126**
*A swing yarder configured for grapple yarding and a loader working in a roadside operation.*

In some situations, cold decks can be used to avoid roadbuilding in difficult areas. Various combinations are feasible: yarding to the cold deck with subsequent yarding to the roadside, yarding and then skidding, or skidding and then yarding. Site-specific conditions will determine what layout will work best for a particular location, and a cost-benefit analysis will help to choose between building the road and "swinging" the timber to an existing road.

## Full or partial suspension

For most cable operations, one end of the logs is lifted off the ground while the other end drags on the ground. This minimizes the stress on the yarder, cables, and anchors. However, some yarders can lift the payload clear above the ground to avoid any disturbance to the soil or residual forest. To achieve full suspension, the appropriate yarder must be used, and the cutblock layout must allow for adequate deflection and clearance.

### OPERATIONAL

When laying out a cutblock for full suspension, the planner must ensure that there is adequate room to accommodate the cable sag, the length of the logs, the height of the carriage, plus the clearance above the residual stand. Various analytical procedures and computer programs are available to calculate the payload for different machines and ground profiles.

The skyline anchors must also be strong enough to support the loads imposed by full suspension. Stumps are usually used for anchors, but fabricated anchors may be required where the stumps are too small or too decayed.

Highlead machines are not typically capable of full suspension because the only way to increase lift is to apply more braking pressure to the haulback. Neither the brakes nor the haulback is designed for the additional stress. A skyline system is usually required for full suspension. Gravity slacklines, slacklines, and running skylines are all capable of full-suspension operations.

**Figure 127**
*Skylines can lift the logs completely free of the ground to clear obstacles.*

**Figure 128**
*The rider block between the haulback and the butt-rigging transforms this highlead yarder into a "scab" skyline configuration to provide additional lift.*

An alternative setup for highlead machines is to use a "scab" skyline that links the butt-rigging with a rider block that runs on the haulback line. This configuration provides more lift than normal, although not as much lift as a full-fledged skyline, and full suspension is feasible only for short distances. However, this skyline causes more wear on the lines and brakes, and is not used extensively.

### ENVIRONMENTAL

Full suspension over sensitive areas may eliminate the need to build roads for accessing those areas. However, the layout must be based on the "total-chance" concept, not just on the single cutblock. By looking at the total layout, the planner is assured that the road eliminated by full-suspension logging today will not be required for tomorrow's adjacent cutblock.

With their capability of fully suspending the payloads, skylines can substatially reduce soil disturbance in sensitive areas, given favourable topography and careful layout. The locations where scouring does occur are limited to spots where deflection is inadequate, and the logs are dragged across the ground. However, full suspension does not imply zero impact. The skyline cable must be lowered to the ground periodically for maintenance, which can do some minor damage to plantations or no-logging zones. Debris may be dropped from the logs into the fly-over zones during inhaul, and the logs come in contact with the ground at the hookup site and the landing.

### Tailhold anchors

Four basic methods are used to anchor the cables at the backline: stump-rigging, backspar trees, mobile tailholds, and alternative anchors.

#### OPERATIONAL

A primary consideration for cable layout is the amount of clearance under the cables at the backline. Highlead systems can operate with little clearance, and the butt-rigging can even drag on the ground over short distances. In contrast, the carriages and grapples for skylines or grapple yarders must be suspended in the air at all times. The type of tailhold determines the amount of clearance under the cables at the backline.

**Figure 129**
*This stump provides a secure anchor for the skyline.*

Stumps work well for highlead anchors. The stumps may be located at the cutblock boundary, or beyond the boundary to increase the clearance. To withstand the cable tension, the stumps must be of adequate size, free of decay, and well rooted. Several stumps can be used together when single stumps are inadequate. Failures of stump anchors are costly and dangerous because of the risk to on-the-ground workers. The *Cable Yarding Systems Handbook* (Workers' Compensation Board 1993) provides information about various rigging methods and stump selection.

**Figure 130**
*Hydraulic excavators are commonly used for backspars with grapple yarders.*

Stumps can also be used for anchors for swing yarders configured for grapple yarding, especially if they are situated on small outcroppings to provide additional clearance for the grapple at the back end. If clearance is inadequate for the grapple, it can be replaced with chokers for the last few metres near the tailhold. If the tailhold is too high above the ground, the grapple will have difficulty reaching the ground to hook the logs.

However, swing yarders configured for grapple yarding operate more quickly than highlead towers, requiring the yarding roads to be changed more often. Mobile tailholds greatly increase the efficiency of changing roads. Hydraulic excavators are preferred over crawler tractors for use as backspars for several reasons: they are more mobile, can easily clear obstacles out of the way, and can position themselves for yarding or travelling by turning the superstructure without spinning the tracks. Stability is provided even without a guyline by resting the bucket on the ground. The boom height provides ground clearance for the grapple adjacent to the backspar. In contrast, crawler tractors cause more soil disturbance because they are turned for every yarding road, and are best suited as backspars when they can remain on the truck roads.

Figure 131
*A skilled worker is required to rig the backspar tree.*

The mobile backspar requires a trail for travelling along the backline. At a minimum, the trail must be cleared of all logs, or may require some minor excavation that maintains natural drainage patterns. Some companies prefer to use the same machine for both trailbuilding and yarding, while others pre-build the trails with a different machine. The advantage of using separate machines is that trails can be built with a machine in better mechanical condition and operated by a worker more experienced with pioneering. During operations, the actual backspar machine simply follows the pre-built trail, with no additional excavation required.

Backspar trees are appropriate for skyline systems in areas of poor deflection, such as near the top of a rounded ridge. The stand must contain trees large and sound enough to serve as backspars, and rigging the tree requires skill that the typical crew may not have. The backspar also provides ground clearance for the carriage at the backline, although this clearance can sometimes be obtained with stump-rigging by extending the skyline into the standing timber beyond the cutblock boundary.

Beyond providing additional clearance at the backline, increasing the anchor height with backspars increases the clearance over the full length of the cable, which can reduce the occurrence of hangups.

In areas where the stumps are inadequate to serve as tailholds, it may be necessary to use alternatives such

Figure 132
*These cables lead to a buried anchor.*

as deadmen, rock bolts, and tipping plates. These methods require some installation time and additional equipment, so they are generally used as a last resort.

ENVIRONMENTAL

Increased backspar height results in increased lift for the payload and less soil disturbance. Depending on deflection, the use of backspars can increase the amount of area available for logging to each landing, and thus reduce the road network requirements.

Mobile backspars may require bladed trails which can increase the amount of soil disturbance. Mats can reduce the amount of excavation required for the backspars.

**Operating period**

The same economic and operational factors apply to nighttime operations with cable systems as to ground-based systems. See the section on ground-based systems for additional information.

**Figure 133**

*Lights on the grapple yarder make nighttime operations feasible.*

OPERATIONAL

Systems that employ on-the-ground workers to hook chokers are limited to daylight operations.

Swing yarders configured for grapple yarding can be operated at night if equipped with adequate lighting. The lights are located at the roadside and must be powerful enough to illuminate all the way to the backline. During inclement weather, it may be difficult to see all the logs to ensure that the utilization standards are being met.

**Protection of the residual stand**

In cable yarding, protection of the residual stand typically refers to partial cutting or to protecting trees outside the actual cutting area. Protection of advance regeneration in a clearcut is difficult with cable systems because the whipping effect of the cables may knock over the small trees. Pulling the logs from the felling site to the corridor ("lateral yarding") may also damage the residual stems.

**Figure 134**

*To minimize damage to the residual stand, the logs are first winched into the skyline corridor using the dropline, and then the carriage and logs are pulled up to the yarder.*

OPERATIONAL

Full-suspension skyline systems can lift logs over plantations located between the road and the cutblock. This can eliminate some road construction through existing plantations.

Falling is difficult and dangerous in partial cuts in large timber because of the overhead hazards. Limbs and tops may break off or the trees may get caught in the residuals. Faller safety is a primary consideration. However, partial cuts can be carried out with conventional equipment (Bennett 1997).

## ENVIRONMENTAL

In partial cutting, protecting the advance regeneration within the cutblock is feasible only with skyline systems. In other systems, the whipping motion of the cable is likely to knock over the residual stems.

**Figure 135**
*This stand was selectively harvested from a series of corridors using a small skyline yarder. The low volume on each road made it feasible to yard with a tower and pile the logs at the roadside without requiring a loader to stay on-site continuously.*

# Aerial Primary Transport

### Destination

Helicopters typically require a central landing for processing the timber and loading trucks. High-production operations may require more than one landing to be used concurrently because the number of logs transported can be too great for a single site.

Landings are usually located on land, but in coastal regions, water drops are commonly used when the cutblocks are located close to a large body of water. Standard procedures such as confinement of floating debris to the landing area must be put into place with water drops.

**Figure 136**
*Water drops are preferred for coastal locations that are within economic flying distance of a suitable drop site.*
Photo courtesy of Helifor Industries Ltd.

Helicopter logging contractors are likely to have individual preferences about landings, which should be discussed and agreed upon early in the planning stage.

#### OPERATIONAL

The landing equipment complement must be matched to the helicopter's production rates because production delays are very costly. All activities should be separated into individual zones to maximize worker safety in the busy environment. The landing must be well organized to remove the timber from the drop zone as soon as possible so the helicopter always has a clear area for landing the timber.

The landing or drop-zone should be situated as close to the cutblock as practical to reduce the flying time. The glide angle should be calculated when the altitude difference between the cutblock and the landing is large — too-steep glide slopes can actually increase the flying time.

#### ENVIRONMENTAL

The size of the landing may become an issue. Planning an area so that one landing can be used for several cutblocks over a period of years will reduce the amount of disturbance.

A plan for debris disposal must be prepared, both for water- and land-based landings. Large amounts of debris can accumulate because a large volume of timber is processed through each landing. Water-based operations must include a provision for confining the debris to the landing area before it is removed.

# Falling

### Tree orientation

Orienting the trees properly for the skidding or yarding phase is one of the most important tasks performed by the faller. As trees are being yarded or skidded, they become aligned with the direction of travel; however, the trees may not "want" to be felled in that direction. Sideslope, tree lean, obstacles, partial cutting prescriptions, and bucking preferences can all influence the falling direction. When that happens, trees must be pulled into alignment as skidding or yarding begins.

**Figure 137**
*Hydraulic jacks may be required for directional control when falling in difficult terrain near sensitive sites.*

Improper alignment reduces productivity for extraction and increases the possibility of stem breakage. Other effects include more soil disturbance, increased damage to residual trees in a partial cut, increased safety hazards, and possible equipment breakage. To minimize these detrimental effects, the falling crew must be aware of the proposed yarding or skidding direction before falling begins, and fall the trees accordingly.

Clearly, feller-bunchers can lay the bunches in almost any orientation, but feller-directors, feller-processors, and hand-fallers can all influence the orientation of the trees. With hand-fallers, directional falling is standard practice — fallers usually use the tree's natural downhill lean as the starting point, and then use wedges to alter the falling direction slightly. In extreme cases, such as near sensitive zones where falling against the natural direction of lean is required, small hydraulic jacks or other mechanical aids may be required to control the falling direction.

In partial cuts, a "herringbone" pattern is commonly used for falling the trees as a compromise between proper alignment for extraction and having the most trees available in each corridor. Trees are felled at an angle towards the corridor to minimize the turning angle once they reach the corridor.

**Figure 138**
*Tree alignment is also important on gentle terrain. By falling the trees across the slope, hookup is easier and productivity is enhanced for yarding with a grapple.*

### Site for bucking

Falling and bucking are often performed by the same worker, especially for cable yarding methods and large timber. Bucking the trees into shorter lengths makes them easier to handle during extraction and minimizes breakage. Furthermore, some trees are simply too large to handle unless they are bucked into logs, or may be too awkward to handle in the landing. These trees must be bucked into logs, but the same rationale does not necessarily apply to every tree for two reasons: safety and overall economics. The severe terrain on some cutblocks precludes bucking — it is simply too dangerous to work — and the trees must be yarded full-length. This situation often results in a congested landing.

However, the effects of the bucking site on total costs are not always as clear. Having the fallers buck the trees into logs means performing a task with a highly paid worker that could be accomplished just as easily on the landing by a lesser-paid worker. Furthermore, the landing bucker may be able to examine the entire tree more easily before bucking, and make a better decision. By bucking at the stump, breakage is reduced and yarding efficiency may be improved, but with additional labour cost for the faller. One FERIC study identified a range of additional cost savings that could accrue to the overall system by waiting until the last possible moment in the harvesting sequence before bucking the trees. The fewer pieces handled at each stage resulted in lower costs, and bucking at the sortyard increased revenues (Araki 1996).

On the other hand, having the faller pre-bunch the trees by hand when yarding very small timber can significantly reduce yarding costs, and be an overall benefit. Each situation should be examined individually to determine the best procedure.

Regardless of the bucking site, the worker must try to maximize the timber value by bucking the tree at the optimal lengths.

### Sorting

Feller-bunchers can be used to sort the trees before skidding. This has little effect on the skidding productivity, but provides a valuable benefit for the processing and loading phases. The timber can be decked at roadside in sorted piles so that neither the processor nor loader must sort. Depending on corporate requirements and the stand characteristics, the sorts can be made according to size, species, or grades.

If the volume per hectare is high enough, sorting during falling could be as simple as dropping the trees into different bunches. With more scattered timber, the feller-buncher may have to accumulate a few stems before travelling a short distance to build a homogenous bunch. The bunches should be properly sized for the skidder to minimize its travel between bunches to accumulate a full load.

Alternatively, the falling can be done in stages by falling and skidding first one sort and then the other. This technique works well for different-size trees — the smaller (more numerous) trees are harvested first to avoid damage and breakage from the larger trees. Multi-pass falling is more expensive because the feller-buncher must travel twice over each section of ground, but the skidding costs do not change.

### Hours of operation

For safety reasons, hand-falling can occur only during daylight hours, but mechanized falling can take place at any hour — lights on the felling equipment provide sufficient illumination to work safely. However, some items such as boundary marks or tree-quality indicators may be overlooked at night, especially during inclement weather. Commonly, daylight hours are used for cutting near the boundaries and nighttime for cutting the interior of the cutblock to reduce the risk of trespassing beyond boundary lines. This approach is especially important along boundaries of riparian zones or other sensitive areas.

### Travel direction

On steep ground, feller-bunchers must travel straight up and down the slope for maximum machine stability, but the feller-buncher can travel in any direction on more gentle terrain. The two options are to travel along the contour (parallel to the road), starting at the back of the cutblock, or to travel perpendicular to the contours and the road. By working along the contour, the upslope area is already cleared, and bunches can be placed in any location with less swing required by the feller-buncher. In contrast, when working perpendicular to the contour, the feller-buncher must swing more, half of the upslope semicircle will always contain standing timber, and the bunches must be placed more carefully. But the perpendicular track provides the advantage of completing the full depth of the cutblock earlier, making it available for skidding. The inventory of felled timber can be reduced with the perpendicular track, a particular advantage for winter logging when snow may bury the felled trees.

## Processing

### Sorting

Sorting decreases the processor efficiency and increases costs — separating the trees prior to skidding can be a better solution than sorting with the processor — but is not always feasible. Various solutions have been devised for sorting in roadside operations, and most involve placing the processed logs at different angles to the road, at different set-backs from the ditchline, or on the opposite side of the road. Each of these methods requires more room than would be required without sorting. Regardless of the method used to distinguish the different sorts, they must provide a clear separation that is obvious to the loader operator.

**Figure 139**
*These logs are sorted into separate piles for sawlogs and pulp in preparation for loading.*

Sorting on the landing can be more or less difficult than at the roadside. With a front-end loader to take the logs away from the processor and enough room to stockpile several sorts on the landing, sorting should be easy. However, with restricted space, or with a swing loader, sorting on the landing becomes more difficult. Full loads of each sort must be set aside before loading, and space may be at a premium.

### Mechanical processing in low-productivity situations

When working on a landing, the processor may be idle for a significant portion of its time if the skidder production is low. The processor is limited to whatever timber is delivered to the landing by the skidders, thus incurring higher costs. Using the same machine for both processing and loading can reduce costs in such circumstances. In one situation, FERIC observed a dangle-head processor loading logs while the regular loader was broken down, and another instance where a stroke delimber was used regularly for loading. The processor loaded the trucks whenever the production fell below four loads per day, but a conventional loader was used at higher levels. While loading, the processor was parked on a ramp behind the trucks that allowed it to reach the full height of the load. FERIC believes that an opportunity exists to design and develop equipment specifically for this multi-function role in low-productivity situations, perhaps by using a quick-connection coupling for a dangle-head processor. The processor head could be replaced with a loading grapple as required.

Without the processor being used in such a multi-function role, processing costs can be improved by operating on several sites close to one another so that skidding, processing, and loading can be segregated. Travel time between sites is an important factor, so having several landings within a single cutblock can be beneficial.

## Loading

### Landing versus roadside
The suitability to landings or roadside methods depends on the type of equipment. Front-end loaders are usually used for landing operations, and are less suited for roadside operations because of their space requirements and their need for a flat travel surface. Swing loaders are more flexible — line and hydraulic loaders can be used for either method, while butt 'n top loaders are designed for roadside operations.

For swing loaders, the roadside terrain influences the choice between landing and roadside methods. A butt 'n top loader can travel on the unprepared surface adjacent to the road in flat terrain, but this may not be possible on steeper terrain. Alternative methods will be required: landings may be required or the loader can load over the cab from the front of the truck (although this procedure is inefficient). Neither method is desirable over an extended time period, but either may be required as a short-term solution.

For cable yarding systems, the choice between roadside and landing operations depends more on the extraction phase than the loading phase. The critical factor for choosing between roadside and landings is the ability for the extraction phase to pile the timber adjacent to the road — line and hydraulic loaders can be used in either situation. On roadside operations on very steep terrain, line loaders, unlike hydraulic loaders, can retrieve logs that may have slipped off the log deck and slid down the hill. Hydraulic loaders have a more limited reach.

### Working on several sites simultaneously
A primary benefit of roadside logging is that it allows the phases to be separated, with each one operating at its own production rate without interference from the other phases. In landing operations, the loading cost is increased compared with roadside because the loader is limited to the production rate of the extraction equipment. Loading costs can be reduced by providing alternative work for the loader, such as a second landing within easy travel distance, or an area for cherry picking or loader-forwarding.

However, several other factors must also be considered: both landings must have enough space to deck the logs safely while the loader is absent, the travel time between sites must not be too long, and the loader must be able withstand the rigours of the extra travel. Hydraulic loaders are suitable for travel between landings or for loader-forwarding, but line loaders are limited to travelling just a few hundred metres.

### Loading direction
The trucking direction must be considered for roadside operations. It is usually best to start loading from the end of each spur, and work towards the beginning. That way, if damage occurs to the road to make it impassable for the log trucks, the loader simply moves towards the beginning of the spur and continues loading. Once repairs to the road are completed, the loader can move back to its original location. A similar technique for soft roads is to partially load the truck from the end of the spur, then move to the beginning to complete the load. This technique can help reduce the ballasting requirements.

Loop roads are another way of improving the trucking efficiency — especially with multi-trailer trucks which are difficult to back up. Loop roads allow them to always travel forwards. However, loop roads also increase the amount of site occupancy by roads.

## Combined Systems

The preceding sections have described the harvesting equipment as if each machine was independent of all the others. In fact, machines are used together as a complete harvesting system. This section will discuss some ways that the equipment in the various phases are used together, and the implications on productivity and environmental concerns.

**Figure 140**
*A stroke delimber operating at the roadside in a full-tree system.*

### Harvesting system descriptions

Harvesting systems can be grouped according to the trees' form during prime transport — either full-tree or manufactured log-lengths. These manufactured logs have two variations depending on the log-lengths. When logs are manufactured between 12 and 25 m long, the system is designated "at-the-stump processing," but when logs about 5–8 m long are produced, the system is commonly called "cut-to-length."

In both types of manufactured log-length systems, the branches and tops are left at the cutting site. On-site debris may require post-harvesting removal to abate the fire hazard or improve the site suitability for regeneration.

The log-manufacturing location influences the equipment selection, as well as the distribution of debris across the landing or cutblock.

***Full-tree system*** In the full-tree system, trees are cut and skidded to the landing before any processing takes place. This system is characteristic of highly mechanized harvesting operations, and is restricted to small timber because of the difficulty of handling large pieces without causing excessive soil disturbance or damage to machinery or timber.

Full-tree systems typically use a feller-buncher with a skidder, clambunk, or yarder. Productivity is high because fewer pieces are handled than with the other systems. The stems are typically topped and delimbed at the landing or road-side using a mechanical delimber, although the logs may be manufactured at a central processing yard in

**Figure 141**
*A stationary delimber and processor located in a central processing yard used in a full-tree harvesting system. The arms and saw in this delimber are controlled remotely from the loader. A chainsaw in the head is used for topping the trees, and a measuring rack located to the left of the delimber measures and cuts the logs to the correct length.*

some full-tree systems. If the logs are transported to a central site for processing, then special trucks may be required and the haul route may not be on public roads.

Debris accumulations must be managed at the manufacturing site, and artificial regeneration is usually required because the tree cones are removed from the cutblock. The full-tree system with roadside or landing-based manufacturing is the most common mechanical system used in the Interior of British Columbia.

The full-tree system is seldom used with partial cutting because of the difficulty of moving long stems between the residual trees.

***At-the-stump processing system***   In at-the-stump processing systems, the trees are topped and cut into logs before being transported to the landing. Logs are typically 15–25 m long.

This system is especially suited to large timber or difficult terrain where mechanized

**Figure 142**
*At-the-stump processing with a conventional stroke delimber. The processed logs are then skidded to the landing.*

falling equipment is unable to operate, so it is often associated with hand-falling and hand-bucking. By manufacturing the trees into logs at the stump, the average piece size is reduced, and the potential for breakage during extraction is reduced. Cutting the trees into smaller logs may be the only practical way to move very large trees without causing excessive soil disturbance.

However, the justification for at-the-stump processing is not restricted just to timber and terrain conditions — other on-block considerations may make it desirable to leave the debris in the cutblock rather than accumulated at the landing. For example, leaving debris on-site may improve nutrient recycling for some ecosystems, improve the regeneration success, or reduce the cost of managing the debris that would otherwise accumulate on the landing. When combined with mechanical falling, at-the-stump processing systems require additional processing equipment to travel to the stump — stroke delimbers, dangle-head delimbers, and delimbing rakes are all possibilities. The amount of debris generated on-site must be monitored; in some situations, heavy debris loading may make regeneration difficult, while in other situations, regeneration may be enhanced.

***Cut-to-length system***   In the cut-to-length (CTL) system, trees are felled and cut into short logs (5–8 m) at the stump, and transported via forwarder to the landing. Cut-to-length systems are typically more expensive in the extraction phase than either full-tree or tree-length systems, and their use is limited to areas where the benefits outweigh the additional harvesting costs. The benefits of cut-to-length can include improved fibre recovery, higher log values, longer operating season, improved secondary transport, reduced silviculture costs, and increased fibre supply.

For mills that consume multiple log-lengths, the CTL system may affect inventory control. In CTL, a computer in the feller-processor makes the bucking decisions, but these decisions are made in the sawmill in tree-length systems. Therefore, the entire log inventory must be consumed by the mill before changes to bucking specifications will be realized. In tree-length systems, the change can be immediate. This means that the inventory for CTL systems should be minimized to retain maximum ability to change log-lengths as required for different market conditions.

On the other hand, changes to the log-length specifications are easy to implement because of the high degree of computerization. Once the computer is updated with new specifications, all subsequent logs will be cut to the new lengths.

Debris is left on-site and is used as a travel mat to support the weight of the forwarders. The debris mat allows the operating season to be extended because it allows for travel over softer ground than would otherwise be feasible.

CTL systems require specialized equipment for all phases from falling through secondary transport. From the equipment owner's perspective, CTL systems require a long-term commitment to acquiring equipment and changing operating procedures; in contrast, full-tree and tree-length systems are interchangeable. Considerable capital investment is required, and CTL cannot be considered for individual cutblocks. From the planner's perspective, CTL can be considered for individual cutblocks only if a market exists for the logs and a contractor with suitable equipment is available upon short notice.

## Between-phase interactions

Harvesting timber can be considered a materials-handling process in which the output from one phase is used as the input for the next phase. Therefore, each phase can influence the operating conditions of the next phase, and the interactions between phases must be considered for maximum efficiency.

*Scheduling*    A common operating technique for reducing costs and increasing the safety factor is to separate the phases so that each machine works at its own best rate without interference from other equipment. If the production rates of the different phases are significantly different from one another, then one of the machines will incur delays and increased costs.

The company and contractor must decide how much inventory to carry between phases because of the carrying costs for the inventory. If the inventory is too large, then the carrying charges will be excessive, but if the inventory is too small, then production delays may occur. The inventory may be only a few hours' production, or it may be several months' production, depending on the site characteristics and the harvesting system.

Roadside systems are well adapted to separating the phases because of the opportunity for stockpiling the timber between the phases. With mechanical systems, falling and skidding are commonly scheduled on the same cutblock, separated by several days' production. In landing-based systems, the skidding, processing, and loading can still be separated, but with more difficulty. Working on several landings simultaneously within one cutblock makes separation of the phases easier. If the cutblocks are small, then several cutblocks within the same general vicinity may be required for efficient operation.

Grapple-equipped machines, both for cable and ground-based equipment, are better suited to roadside operations than choker-equipped machines, and thus, better able to separate the phases.

On steep sites harvested with cable systems, it is typical to fall the entire cutblock before starting yarding because of the safety hazard; falling and yarding simultaneously on steep terrain is dangerous. Falling and yarding may occur simultaneously on a cutblock on gentle terrain if there is enough distance between the falling and yarding crews.

***Optimizing the timber for subsequent phase*** Optimizing the timber for the subsequent phase implies that the timber is oriented correctly, is bunched or sorted as required, is placed in an accessible location, and has minimal breakage. These conditions are determined by both operating techniques and equipment selection, and require clear communications between workers so that everybody knows the requirements of the following phase. Considering each phase in isolation will lead to inefficient harvesting.

**Figure 143**

*Poor communication between the falling and skidding crews resulted in excessive soil disturbance on this site. The timber was skidded up the adverse grade to a road located at the top of the ridge — it could have been skidded down the draw to the right, avoiding the adverse grade, if the timber had been felled differently.*

The most critical interaction is usually between the falling and extraction phases because falling offers the greatest opportunity to vary the orientation of the timber. If the timber is oriented incorrectly, then every tree will require turning before skidding, which may result in increased soil disturbance and production delays. In partial cutting, improper orientation can also increase damage to the residual stand. The faller must be aware of the proposed extraction direction, and orient the timber accordingly.

It may be beneficial to use a more expensive machine for one phase if a greater payback can be realized at a following phase. For example, mechanical falling is more expensive than hand-falling, but mechanical falling allows for the use of more efficient skidders. Without bunching, line skidders are required because grapple skidders are ineffective. The cost reduction for grapple skidding is enough to compensate for the increased cost for mechanical falling. Another example is to use a loader-forwarder to build bunches for a grapple yarder or grapple skidder to improve the skidding efficiency.

A range of slopes and site conditions may be too steep for ground-based skidding equipment, but not too steep for mechanical falling equipment. Cable yarding systems are then required. In such situations, using a feller-buncher with a swing yarder configured for grapple yarding may be more efficient than using hand-fallers and a highlead yarder.

**Figure 144**

*Trees were felled by hand then bunched with an loader for skidding with a grapple skidder. Productivity for the skidder was increased by the bunching.*

Timber breakage can occur at any point in the harvesting process, and the value losses are cumulative. Equipment selection and operating techniques that reduce the breakage will result in increased value of the delivered timber. The effect on profit is not so clear — the benefit of increased value must be weighed against the additional cost of recovering the fibre. More timber can often be extracted from a stand by using feller-bunchers or feller-processors because of the reduced breakage compared with hand-falling. The reduced breakage occurs both in the falling and skidding phases.

Breakage may incur a liability that must be addressed later. For example, careless falling near gullies may result in additional cleanup costs to remove the debris from the gully.

# SITE AND STAND CHARACTERISTICS

Site and stand characteristics, as opposed to characteristics defined by the planners and operators, are inherent to the site. These characteristics influence the success of using a particular class of equipment. Over the long term, the general site and stand characteristics that are expected must be examined, and the equipment fleet selected to suit those conditions. The time horizon for selecting the equipment is related to budget and capital amortization issues, and is generally three to five or more years.

Contractual and corporate obligations mean there is less flexibility to choose different equipment in the short term, and the equipment selection question is reversed. The site and stand characteristics remain important, but instead of asking "What equipment is suited to this site?" the question becomes "What site is available to use this equipment?" The process of matching equipment to sites becomes a matter of ensuring an adequate quantity of suitable sites for the available equipment.

These site and stand characteristics are divided into four broad classes for discussion: terrain, soil, timber, and weather and climate.

## Terrain

Terrain, especially the sideslope, has the most influence on machine selection. In general, cable systems are more commonly used on coastal sites with steep sideslopes, while ground-based systems are more common in the Interior, where slopes are less steep. Although other factors such as soil texture and climate also influence the choice between cable and ground systems, terrain is the predominant factor.

Other important terrain factors are ground profile, riparian areas, gullies, and roughness.

### Slope
Slope is the predominant factor in choosing between cable and ground-based equipment. In addition, slope can be an important factor in determining the suitability of different machine types, especially for ground-based equipment.

Although the average sideslope for the entire cutblock is the measure used most often to describe a cutblock, the maximum slope plus the amount of area over which these maximum slopes occur are also important. For ground-based systems, small areas with steep slopes do not always mean that a different machine must be selected, because the effect of steep slope can often be reduced with different operating techniques. For example, short, steep slopes can be harvested with directional falling and reaching from the side, or by straight-downslope skidding. But when the extent of steep terrain increases beyond just isolated patches, the machine selection for the entire cutblock may be affected.

**Figure 145**
*Clambunks are quite stable and can work on steeper ground than rubber-tired skidders.*

Slope influences the safe working envelope for ground-based equipment. Wheeled equipment can work safely on slopes to about 35%, while tracked machines can work up to about 50%. Specialized tracked machines can work on steeper ground, while loader-forwarders are limited to about 30%. Forwarders have a high centre of gravity, and become unstable if positioned crossways on the sideslope. They are limited to slopes of about 35%. Clambunks are quite stable, and can work on slopes up to 60%.

Ground-based equipment works more efficiently when skidding downhill, and adverse skidding should usually be avoided. Forwarders, clambunks, and tracked skidders can tolerate more adverse skidding than wheeled skidders, although their production will be reduced with adverse skidding.

Slope affects cable machines differently than ground-based equipment — there is not the same distinction of machine types by slope classes because each machine type can work on all slope ranges if deflection is adequate. Cable yarding systems usually work better for uphill yarding, although either direction is feasible. Gravity systems require about 30% sideslope for the carriage to return to the hookup site.

Very steep or broken terrain (> 70%) can increase the amount of breakage during falling and yarding and decrease the mobility of on-the-ground workers. Building suitable landings is difficult on steep slopes, so the layout must consider landing location. The landing area must provide sufficient space to land and unhook the logs without them sliding back into the cutblock. When suitable landing locations are not available, alternate systems must be considered.

**ENVIRONMENTAL**

Ground-based skidding on steep ground may require bladed skid trails, which are a source of soil disturbance and can intercept and concentrate water flow resulting in erosion and sedimentation.

## Ground profile

The ground profile indicates the general shape of the ground as viewed across the contours. Profile is different from roughness, which is described later. The ground profile can be considered over the full width of the cutblock, or for an intermediate distance (30–150 m). Both the overall and intermediate profiles affect cable systems, while the overall profile does not affect ground-based systems as much.

**OPERATIONAL**

Since cables hang in an arc, a concave ground profile is optimal to use cable systems. The measure of the ground profile to provide adequate space for the cable sag is called "deflection." Deflection is measured as a percentage of the horizontal distance between the two ends of the cable. For short distances and light payloads, 6% deflection may be adequate, but for larger payloads, up to 15% deflection may be required. Depending on the type of cable system, up to 25 m of clearance is required below the cable to accommodate the carriage, chokers, grapple, and logs.

The harvesting area must be planned carefully by running deflection lines across the critical zones. The analysis should not be limited to just the specific cutblock; adjacent areas should be examined as well to ensure that the road network will be useful and adequate for future cutblocks. Various analytical methods and computer programs can help the planner to calculate the deflection and payload before road construction or harvesting operations commence.

With adequate deflection and clearance, the cables hang clear of the ground from the yarder to the tailhold, which maximizes yarding efficiency by minimizing hangups. Fewer hangups also results in reduced soil disturbance. Even or convex profiles are difficult to harvest with cable systems, and may require backspars or multi-span skylines to cover the area. On uneven slopes or broken ground, more road may be required to provide access to all locations.

Uneven profiles are less of a problem with ground-based systems than with cable systems because the machines can travel on the benches between the steeper areas. Depending on the size and type of machine, they may be able to reach the timber on the steeper areas while remaining on the benches. Trails will be required to link the various benches with the landing or haul road.

## ENVIRONMENTAL

For cable systems, areas with poor deflection may experience increased soil disturbance. For ground-based systems, the number and distribution of benches and ridges will influence skidding patterns, including the location and extent of skid trails, which may affect the amount of soil disturbance.

## Riparian areas

Riparian areas occur next to the banks of streams, lakes, wetlands, and gullies and include both the area dominated by continuous high moisture content and the adjacent upland vegetation that exerts an influence on it. These generally sensitive sites may have different forest management requirements than the remaining cutblock, and warrant using alternative harvesting techniques. For example, there may be a requirement to leave standing trees, fall and yard away from the stream, or leave machine-free buffers. In British Columbia, the Forest Practices Code's *Riparian Management Area Guidebook* describes a method for identifying and assessing these areas and recommended management practices. Riparian management areas, as defined in the guidebook, always include a management

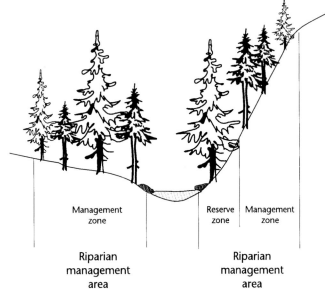

Management
zone

Reserve
zone

Management
zone

Riparian
management
area

Riparian
management
area

**Figure 146**
*Riparian management areas always include a management zone, but may also include a reserve zone.*

zone, where constraints may be applied to harvesting, and may include a reserve zone, where harvesting is generally prohibited. The width of the reserve zone and management zone depends on the classification of the stream, lake, or wetland. The procedures for determining the width are described fully in the guidebook.

Harvesting operations within the management zone should minimize disturbance to the understorey vegetation, avoid damage to any remaining trees, and maintain bank stability. Limit the amount of disturbance to that required to achieve successful regeneration.

Proper falling techniques are the key to successful harvesting operations in riparian areas. Either manual or mechanical methods can be used, but the capabilities of the extraction equipment must be carefully considered before falling commences. Hydraulic loaders have been used to control the direction of large, high-value trees by holding the tree while it is cut by the faller.

**Figure 147**

*This loader held the tree as it was cut by the faller. Once the faller moved out of the danger zone, the loader pulled the tree away from the reserve zone located behind the standing trees.*

Line skidders winch individual trees without travelling into the riparian areas if the trees are aligned properly. This technique implies closely supervised hand-falling to ensure that the faller knows the required skidding direction. Grapple skidders have limited reach, so they are inappropriate to use with hand-falling. Many logging contractors, even those that rely upon grapple skidders, have a line skidder on site for use in such situations.

Grapple skidders or clambunks can be used for harvesting riparian areas if the trees are small enough for feller-bunchers to pack them after cutting. Depending on the soil conditions, feller-bunchers can travel into the zone, cut the trees, and transport them out of the zone with minimal soil disturbance. A zero-clearance feller-buncher will minimize the width required for the trail. Close supervision is required to ensure that the skidder operators do not follow the feller-buncher's trail into areas where they are prohibited.

In some cases, loader-forwarders are permitted into riparian areas to retrieve individual trees. Careful maneuvering is required to move the trees out of the zone without damaging the residuals. FERIC spoke to one company that reported that its loader-forwarder lifted the trees back to vertical to make it easier to move them through the residual stand.

**Figure 148**

*Logs were fully suspended over this management zone to a landing on the opposite side of the stream. The profile allows for adequate deflection and clearance.*

Using cable equipment around riparian areas implies careful consideration to the tailhold location. Skyline systems can span the zone if the ground profile beyond the zone provides sufficient elevation to raise the cables above the standing timber. A slackpulling carriage must be used so that the skyline can remain tensioned at all times. Note that the skyline may be lowered occasionally for maintenance, and it may cause damage to residual trees and other vegetation. With highlead or grapple systems, the cables are continually raised and lowered, so tailholds beyond the management zone are unworkable. Locating the tailholds on the near side of the management zone implies that all the borderline trees must be away from the zone to be within reach of the chokers or grapple. Careful directional falling is required.

Machine operations within riparian areas must be done with minimal soil disturbance. The operators must be made aware of the importance of proceeding slowly and carefully. Dry conditions with low ground-pressure equipment will minimize the risk of creating ruts, as will frozen conditions or deep snow.

The residual trees should be chosen to present a windfirm boundary to avoid future soil disturbance caused by windthrow. Various techniques such as topping, pruning, or edge modification will reduce the sail area of the residual trees and reduce the risk of windthrow.

## Gullies

Gullies — steep streams that run within steep-sided and deep channels — are sensitive areas that may require special management considerations. Debris flows and debris floods are of concern in gullies. Site factors that can affect the level of these hazards include steepness of gully sidewalls, availability of loose material, stream gradient, and the drainage basin area. Harvesting-related factors include the amount of soil disturbance during yarding, volumes of debris left in the gully, removal of stabilizing trees, unstable road crossings, and poor drainage control.

**Figure 149**
*The tailhold for this yarder was located across the gully. The skyline enabled the machine to lift the logs out of the gully without causing soil disturbance.*

In British Columbia, the Forest Practices Code's *Gully Assessment Procedures Guidebook* provides information on assessment procedures for coastal sites, and describes management objectives and pre-logging strategies when operating in gully areas on the Coast. The areas adjacent to gullies can also include riparian areas, with associated management requirements, which may have to be considered along with any special measures required for gully management.

In many cases, the riparian management zone adjacent to a gully will allow only partial cutting. Therefore, selection of harvesting equipment for working near gullies should be based on systems that work well close to standing timber or for partial cutting. This results in some unique requirements for the harvesting equipment. The selected equipment must be able to:

- remain outside the harvesting zone while still reaching the timber;
- extract timber from steep ground;
- extract the crop trees without damage to the residual trees;
- extract trees without causing excessive soil disturbance to gully sidewalls; and
- minimize the amount of logging debris entering the gully.

In addition, the equipment may be required to remove debris from the gully if it accumulates in the channel.

Workers' safety must be a priority when logging in or around gullies. Steep slopes, leaning trees, slippery footing, and productivity concerns compound one another to make gullies extremely hazardous workplaces. The hazards and risks must be examined carefully and a safe procedure agreed upon before harvesting.

### OPERATIONAL

Falling within the gullies is limited to non-mechanical methods. The trees must be felled carefully in the desired location, whether cross-slope to minimize breakage and debris accumulation in the gully, or upslope to minimize the distance to the gully edge. Uphill falling is difficult and dangerous, and will require hydraulic jacks or other means to control the falling direction.

**Figure 150**
*A swing yarder with its lines extended over a gully.*

Line skidders are well suited for working around gullies, provided that the ground adjacent to the gully is suitable for ground-based machine travel. The skidder can be positioned near the gully edge and the cable pulled out to reach the logs. Similarly, large loader-forwarders can reach the logs from the gully edge without entering the gully. Grapple skidders, forwarders, and clambunks are poorly suited for logging from gullies because of their limited reach.

Tightly spaced gullies, or other no-travel zones, will make skidding difficult because the machines must be able to work between gullies without encroaching on them; also, logs must not sweep into the gullies while turning. During falling, the trees should be aligned with the skidding direction to ensure that the minimum amount of space is required for turning the logs. Bucking the trees into short logs may be required. Gullies and other no-travel zones spaced closer than two tree lengths are difficult areas to harvest.

When harvesting in gullies, cable systems are better suited than ground-based systems (i.e., yarders can remain outside the gully while reaching the logs). In contrast, ground-based systems must travel closer to reach the logs. However, the cables must remain clear of standing timber, which differentiates partial cutting and clearcutting. With partial cutting, the cables must be suspended above or to the side of the standing timber, while in clearcutting, the cables can be positioned within the gully itself. For partial cutting, skyline systems with slackpulling carriages are well suited, while any cable system can be used for clearcutting.

With skylines and slackpulling carriages, the deflection and payload must be examined carefully, and correct bucking procedures used to ensure that the yarder can extract the logs. "Sideblocking" will allow the logs to be pulled out of the gully to underneath the skyline before yarding them to the landing. This technique requires a carriage that can be clamped to the skyline during lateral yarding.

Debris accumulations within the gullies must be managed. Chokers are less efficient than grapples for picking up large volumes of debris because a worker must take the time to hook each bundle of debris. Other removal methods, such as hand piling the debris and removing it with a choker or post-harvest removal by helicopter, may be more efficient for small volumes.

When logging is permitted in gullies, the trees must be extracted without scouring the gully sidewalls, and debris accumulations must be removed. With cable systems, this puts two requirements on the system design: (1) the chokers or grapple must be able to reach into the gully to hook the logs, and (2) the lift should be maximized to enable lifting the logs clear of the ground.

Using slackpulling carriages is the best method for reaching into a gully with chokers because the skyline can remain tensioned while the dropline is spooled out to reach the logs. With a grapple or a highlead system, lowering the lines and spotting them accurately in a steep gully is difficult. Interlocked winches make it easier to control the grapple accurately within the gully.

The ability to lift the logs is directly related to the deflection, so the deflection near gullies should be maximized. Tall yarders, backspar trees, short yarding distances, and suitable ground profile can all increase the deflection. Yarding distance and ground profile are influenced by road and landing location, so careful layout will help ensure proper placement.

However, there are competing factors for landing placement and the subsequent yarding direction with respect to the gully. Locating the landing inside the gully gives a "clear view" up or down the gully, and maximizes deflection. However, the debris accumulations at the landing are unacceptable. Moving the landing to outside the gully improves the debris situation, but reduces deflection and lift.

## Roughness

Ground roughness is independent of slope. It is a measure of the height and spacing of obstacles that affect the ride and stability of ground-based equipment and the ability of cable equipment to yard efficiently. Typical obstacles that impede the machines' travel are rocks, boulders, depressions, outcrops, large stumps, and windfalls.

### OPERATIONAL

Rough ground can cause instability, and a lower centre of gravity can be an advantage. The logs dragged by skidders tend to enhance their stability, while the high carrying position of the load for forwarders tends to reduce their stability.

Ground-based equipment must also be able to maneuver efficiently between the obstacles while transporting the payload. Forwarders are better able than skidders to maneuver between obstacles because the short logs do not drag over the obstacles during turns. Full-length logs behind a skidder are less maneuverable.

Large stumps and boulders can cause hangups for cable systems. Swing yarders are better able to yard around obstacles because they can alter the location of the cable slightly by swinging slightly off-centre.

# Soil

### Texture and moisture content

Soil texture and moisture content, two of the most important soil characteristics, affect the soil's ability to support machine traffic and resist degradation. Various processes can degrade soil, including:

- soil compaction and puddling;

- soil displacement;

- forest floor displacement;

- surface soil erosion; and

- mass wasting.

The sensitivity of a site to these processes depends on a number of factors such as terrain, slope, climate, hydrology, and soil horizons, texture and depth. Once this information is known, management practices can be implemented to ensure that the effects of these processes are minimized. This generally involves placing limits on the

*Figure 151*
*Puddling and compaction from excessive machine traffic during wet weather.*

amount and types of soil disturbances caused by harvesting and silviculture treatments. Soil disturbance is generally higher, and therefore more of a concern, with ground-based harvesting systems than with cable systems.

In British Columbia, under the Forest Practices Code, soil disturbance hazard assessments are carried out on some sites to help make certain management decisions based on the sensitivity of a site to soil degradation. The procedures for carrying out these assessments, along with some related management concerns, are described in the *Hazard Assessment Keys for Evaluating Site Sensitivity to Soil Degrading Processes Guidebook*. For jurisdictions other than British Columbia, these processes or other similar processes may be used. An exact description of what systems to use and where is beyond the scope or intent of this hand-

*Figure 152*
*Using wide tires on a skidder during winter logging on Vancouver Island.*

book — its purpose is to highlight the important issues and encourage the reader to seek expert advice, especially in marginal situations.

Both soil moisture and soil texture play a role in the soil's ability to withstand machine or equipment impacts without being degraded. Neither factor can be changed to suit harvesting requirements, but soil moisture is partially within the manager's control by scheduling the harvesting operations for when the moisture content is lowest, such as summer or early fall. For ground-based equipment, the sensitivity to compaction is commonly used as a guideline for equipment selection and operating techniques, particularly when operating on gentle slopes and uniform terrain. Areas with high compaction hazard are usually restricted to harvesting on dry or frozen conditions, or with deep snow cover, or no ground-based equipment is permitted to operate on the site. Seasonal impacts are discussed later in this section. On steeper slopes where machines often operate on trails, displacement and mass wasting hazards become more important.

The soil moisture and texture must be considered together because soil moisture affects each soil type differently. Sandy soils are not easily compacted, even when moist; in contrast, loamy soils are susceptible to compaction when moist but are more resistant to compaction when dry. Fine-textured soils such as clays and silts are susceptible to compaction even at low soil moisture contents.

Soil texture plays an important role in determining these detailed hazard ratings. However, FERIC observed during the interview process that operational personnel such as woods managers and logging supervisors typically used less precise descriptions of soil types. Terms such as "winter ground" versus "summer ground" or "fine-textured soils" versus "coarse-textured soils" were commonly used by operational personnel, instead of the detailed soil hazard ratings specified in the British Columbia guidebooks.

### OPERATIONAL

When using ground-based equipment, the operators must be prepared to reschedule their activities if the soil moisture content becomes too high, such as during heavy precipitation. Attitudes regarding soil disturbance have changed substantially over the past few years; FERIC was told many times during the interviews that contractors and opera-

**Figure 153**
*The tracks on this forwarder facilitate travel on softer ground compared with just tires.*

tors have become much more diligent about policing their own activities. Some companies have established guidelines for shutdown criteria during wet weather, and have distributed these guidelines to their contractors. It is not uncommon for the contractors or operators to cease operations on their own accord.

As an alternative to shutting down, the harvesting pattern for the whole cutblock should be examined and planned for maximum flexibility. Preserving the drier areas for wetter weather may help to avoid shutdowns. This strategy has minimal cost even if the heavy rain does not occur, and may make the difference between working and not if the rain does happen. Other techniques are to confine skidding to bladed trails or to cease trucking in favour of stockpiling the timber during heavy precipitation.

High moisture content and fine soil texture often occur together, such as near swamps, where the soils are moist and have low bearing capacity. Some alternatives to using conventional ground-based equipment are to schedule the harvesting under frozen conditions, to use low ground-pressure equipment such as feller-processors and forwarders, or to use cable equipment.

As discussed elsewhere in the handbook, using specialized equipment is seldom economical for just one cutblock — it must be part of an overall plan that includes amortization of fixed costs. The planner must calculate the amount of timber that would become available for harvesting with the different equipment, and the effect of adding the new equipment on costs and length of operating season. Only a thorough examination will reveal whether alternative equipment will be justified.

**ENVIRONMENTAL**

Given a particular type of equipment, controlling the soil moisture via scheduling can be used to affect the amount of soil disturbance. The susceptibility to compaction generally increases with soil moisture, and surface water can cause erosion. All other things being equal, soil disturbance will be lower with dry soils than with moist soils.

The aerial and cable systems can work under conditions with high soil moisture content without causing excessive soil disturbance. This is especially true for the skyline systems that can lift the payload clear of the ground. Highlead systems may cause more soil disturbance than other cable systems because they must drag one end of the log on the ground.

## Seasonal impact

The seasonal impact on soil is typically reversed between interior and coastal locations. Winter in the Interior brings frozen conditions, when access is least restricted. When the snowpack is light, the frozen ground can support vehicles without rutting or compaction. Deep snow can also protect the soil from damage, although it can also act as an insulator to prevent the soil from freezing if heavy snowfall occurs too early in the season. In such cases, deep snow may not provide sufficient protection from soil disturbance. Summer and the transition periods before and after summer usually produce the most concern about soil disturbance.

On the other hand, winter and its transition periods are the critical times for soil disturbance on the Coast because of higher rainfalls. The soil is rarely frozen for a sustained period at the low elevations where most winter operations take place.

**OPERATIONAL**

Winter is the least expensive time for harvesting in the Interior because of the easier access caused by frozen conditions. However, deep snow can impair the mobility of wheeled skidders, to the point where tracked machines are required to construct access

**Figure 154**
*Traction in deep, powdery snow was difficult for this forwarder.*

trails. Forwarders with tandem axles and tracks are less susceptible to deep snow than skidders, although very deep snow will also reduce their mobility. The snow also changes characteristics throughout the winter season; early in the season, the snow is typically dry and powdery ("sugary"), and offers little traction. Later in the season as the snow begins to melt and becomes more dense, it offers better traction. Late winter, when the snow is most compact, is a prime time for ground-based skidding in the Interior.

On the Coast, winter offers less favourable conditions for logging because of the inclement weather. High precipitation, high winds, and saturated soils increase the risk of slope failures on steep slopes. Fallers cannot work during windy conditions, so the frequency of non-productive days increases in the winter. Trucking becomes difficult because of steep, icy roads.

### ENVIRONMENTAL

The most critical time for soil disturbance in the Interior is the transition period before and after summer. Low millyard inventories after spring breakup may result in corporate pressure to begin harvesting operations when the soil moisture content may be high. The highest levels of supervision are required at these times to avoid poor operating practices. In the fall, high precipitation levels may saturate the soil, which increases the risk of soil disturbance. After a summer of dry conditions, the operators may be unprepared for working under more critical conditions.

Soft-footprint machines such as feller-processors and forwarders are advantageous during the transition period because they can operate with less soil disturbance than conventional ground-based equipment such as skidders. With less seasonal "stop-and-go," forwarder operators may also be more prepared to using the proper operating techniques.

Wide tires or tracks mounted over the tires can also reduce ground pressure and soil disturbance.

Operators must not be deceived by snow on the ground because the snow can simply be masking unfrozen soil. If the weather before the snowfall has not been cold for long enough, then the ground may not be frozen and the snow will act as an insulator, preventing any additional freezing. In such a case, the snow must be deep and compactible enough to distribute the machine's weight over a wide area to prevent soil compaction.

For coastal areas where the harvesting plan includes ground-based harvesting with skidders, the driest periods during the summer offer the best conditions for minimizing environmental impact. Loaders used as loader-forwarders and mobile backspars can work year-round in many locations, but must always avoid localized areas of wet or sensitive soils.

There may be short periods during the winter on the Coast where the temperature drops below freezing for a sustained time, and the ground becomes sufficiently frozen to support harvesting equipment without rutting and compaction. However, the proper permits must already be in place to take advantage of these infrequent opportunities, and close supervision must be undertaken to ensure that operations cease if conditions change.

## Timber Characteristics

Timber can be characterized by the tree size, stand volume, and quality. For each characteristic, the cutblocks have an average value and a range of values, both of which affect the machine's ability to operate effectively.

The long-term timber resource must be examined, and equipment selected that best balances between low operating cost and flexibility to adapt to the full range of timber characteristics. In some cases, the timber characteristics have minimal impact on the equipment's ability to operate (e.g., grapple skidder), while in other cases, a mismatch between equipment and timber will prevent the equipment from operating at all (e.g., feller-processor in large timber).

### Tree size

Tree size affects logging equipment in two distinct ways: (1) its physical ability to lift and process the tree; and (2) the operating cost. Larger trees require larger equipment to withstand the stresses involved with lifting heavy payloads, while smaller trees require machines that will not cause excessive log breakage. Larger trees usually result in lower operating costs, within the physical limitations of the equipment to handle the tree. The exact relationship depends on the type of equipment and its application.

*Figure 155*
*This large processor from Vancouver Island can easily handle second-growth logs.*

Tree size can be measured several ways, such as volume, diameter, height, and weight. A discussion of volume per hectare, a characteristic of the stand that is related to tree size, follows.

**OPERATIONAL**

Machines that lift and support the tree during the processing cycle are most affected by tree size, while machines that simply move the trees are less affected. For example, feller-bunchers are typically used for trees up to about 1 m³ because larger trees are too heavy for most feller-bunchers to lift. Beyond that size requires the use of hand-fallers or feller-directors that do not fully support the trees. This action has a ripple effect on the subsequent phases; for example, grapple skidders and clambunks are most effective when used with feller-bunchers.

*Figure 156*
*Smaller logs allow the use of smaller equipment.*

In addition to the size limit caused by lifting capacity, some machines are limited to maximum diameter, while others can handle a wide range of sizes. For example, feller-bunchers and processors are limited by the size of their saws or grab-arms, and it is not uncommon to encounter trees larger than the machine's capacity. Such trees must be handled by alternate means such as hand-fallers or hand-buckers. On the other hand, equipment such as grapple yarders and line loaders can handle almost any size of tree, although some sizes are handled more efficiently than others. A tree too large for these machines to handle is rare.

Occasional large logs can be handled as an exception by most systems, but a steady supply of oversized trees increases wear and tear and maintenance. The equipment must be selected to efficiently handle the largest tree that will be routinely encountered, and provisions made to handle the oversized trees.

Smaller trees can also have an impact on a machine's effectiveness, especially regarding physical damage to the trees. Large grapple yarders or line loaders ineffectively handle small trees because their grapples are so heavy that it is difficult to avoid breakage without unacceptable losses in productivity. With mechanical falling, feller-processors are more exacting machines than feller-bunchers, and are less likely to be used to push over small trees. Instead, each tree is cut individually, even if quite small, which can lead to increased utilization of small stems.

However, the issue with small trees is not so much the physical capability of the machine, but the operating costs. Many harvesting operations require trees to be handled individually, which produces higher costs with smaller trees. Small trees usually require less time for processing, but the unit cost increases substantially because of the reduced volume.

Various techniques for bunching and handling several trees simultaneously have been devised to counteract the trend for increased costs for smaller trees. However, efficiencies gained at one phase may come at the expense of higher operating costs for another phase. For example, the advantage of grapple skidders compared with line skidders is that they can hook and unhook many logs very quickly. However, grapple skidders require the use of a feller-buncher to work efficiently; therefore, falling costs are increased compared with hand-falling. Grapple skidders would be uneconomic to operate without the added expense of a feller-buncher, but together, they are effective.

Manufacturers recognize the effect of tree size by producing a range of products in different size classes. The smaller machines are built lighter because they do not experience the same stress loads; therefore, they have lower ground pressure. The owner and the equipment dealer must carefully examine the timber resource and match it to the size class.

The interaction between tree size and terrain features can influence machine selection. For example, many stands of small trees are within the economic harvesting range for mechanical systems, but grow on sites too steep for skidders, so different primary transport equipment is required. Swing yarders configured for grapple yarding or clambunk skidders may be viable options, but they both require feller-bunchers. Although feller-bunchers can work on steeper terrain than skidders, they also have limits. Without a feller-buncher, hand-falling would be required, which may make these systems uneconomic.

### ENVIRONMENTAL

Larger tree size may lead to increased soil disturbance if the machine cannot support the log adequately.

## Volume per hectare and total cutblock volume

The issues of volume per hectare and cutblock volume are based largely on amortization of fixed costs.

### OPERATIONAL

The fixed costs for moving into a cutblock must be amortized over the cutblock volume. Larger cutblocks result in lower unit operating costs, and for a given cutblock size, higher volumes per hectare result in lower costs. In general, the more mobile the equipment, the more able it is to deal with lower volumes.

In cable yarding, each yarding road also has a setup cost to be amortized. This cost makes cable yarding more sensitive to volumes per hectare than ground-based skidding. Machines with shorter setup times can operate more economically in stands with lower volumes per hectare than machines with longer setup times.

Lower volumes per hectare also require greater lengths of road to develop the same volume of timber, which increases the amortization cost for road development.

### ENVIRONMENTAL

With lower stand volumes, more roads are required to harvest the same volume of timber which may lead to increased risk of sedimentation, and other environmental impacts that originate from roads.

## Quality

Timber quality is a concern in the log-manufacturing process. Log manufacturing includes removing the branches, topping the trees, removing rot and defect, cutting the

**Figure 157**
*Does the timber quality warrant hand- or mechanical falling and processing methods?*

logs to length, and sorting. The objective is to produce logs acceptable to the mill from the existing timber resource at an acceptable cost. Higher-quality trees require less processing and produce less debris to be managed.

Timber quality, although important, is not usually the primary driving factor in choosing equipment for log

manufacturing. More important is how the manufacturing process fits into the overall harvesting system, including final delivery to the mill.

Trees can be processed into logs at different locations, including a central processing yard, roadside, landing, or stump. The choice of processing location is a long-term decision that affects the equipment selection. Once the decision is made and appropriate equipment acquired, there is limited flexibility to change the location.

The type of equipment influences the size and location of debris piles, a by-product of log manufacturing. Issues such as nutrient recycling from branches and needles, roadside compaction, debris disposal, and net plantable area are all affected by the choice of processing location.

Since tree quality is a factor mainly in the processing phase, the discussion will focus primarily on the processors, even though log quality should be considered for all phases. Any changes made to the log-manufacturing processes must consider the impacts on the other phases.

The most basic choice for processing methods is whether to use manual or mechanical methods, a choice governed largely by other factors such as terrain or tree size. However, quality does have an effect (e.g., small, limby trees with abundant decay would be better suited to mechanical processing because of the amount of labour required for hand-bucking). In very decadent stands, safety hazards such as rotten tops and branches can fall on the hand-fallers. This is especially true in partial cutting systems, when making the initial opening in a clearcut, or when falling the right-of-way for road construction. Hand-fallers and buckers can examine each log individually to make the best falling or bucking decision. In selection systems, the crop trees are chosen according to visual clues that may be difficult to see from the cab of a feller-buncher. Hand-falling may be required to achieve the quality objectives. With a properly trained grader-bucker, the value of high-value trees can be further increased by proper bucking. Mechanical falling and processing are better suited to uniform or lower-value trees that are treated more as a commodity.

With mechanical processors, the dangle-head machines tend to work better with small trees with small branches as compared with stroke delimbers for larger trees with larger limbs. The drive systems used on dangle-head processors to move the logs through the head tend to slip on the trees with large limbs, but the strokers have a better grip. Depending on the

**Figure 158**
*The fast processing time on this small dangle-head processor makes it well suited to small-diameter trees.*

method used for encoding the length-measuring information, slippage may cause inaccurate readings and require the log to be reprocessed to obtain a correct length measurement. Even without the complications caused by slippage, length-measuring equipment must be calibrated regularly to ensure proper operation.

Dangle-head processors cut the log to length after just one pass over the stem, while strokers usually make two passes before cutting the log. Thus, strokers can examine the entire log for defect (either visually or mechanically) before making the bucking decision, and should make a better decision. However, this distinguishing characteristic may not be important in stands with smaller trees, where the bucking decision is based on top diameter.

Sorting may be a concern in multi-species stands, or stands with many different products. Sorting by mechanical processing at roadside is limited to two or three sorts, but sorting on landings is usually done with a second machine such as a front-end loader, and the total number of sorts can often be increased. Depending on the landing size and configuration, six or more sorts may be feasible.

Feller-processors used in cut-to-length systems are efficient at removing mid-stem decay that may otherwise go unnoticed until the log reaches the mill. By removing the decay as soon as possible after felling, the amount of unusable material that is transported through the system is minimized. On the other hand, feller-processors are more fragile than feller-bunchers, and less liable to be used for pushing over undersized trees. Instead, each tree must be cut individually, which provides the incentive to make a log from the tree. Utilization can be improved from stands with a high percentage of small trees by using feller-processors.

Windfall can affect the choice of equipment and methods. Safety is a primary concern, especially for hand-fallers. Rootwads can easily crush a worker if proper precautions are not taken. Mechanical falling is much safer, but the equipment must be large enough to handle the tree size. Feller-buncher heads with high-rotation side-tilt can improve productivity compared with the regular felling heads because they can align with stems lying in many different directions, such as might happen after a windstorm.

### ENVIRONMENTAL

Debris disposal is influenced by timber quality — the more decay, defect, and branches on the trees, the more debris generated. The consequence of more debris will vary depending on the processing location (i.e., at the stump, roadside, landing, or central sortyard).

With at-the-stump processing, the tops and branches remain on the site, and their nutrients are eventually recycled into the soil. However, the tops and branches may also interfere with silviculture treatment or present a fire hazard; the relative importance of these issues will vary depending on the local requirements. At-the-stump processing can be accomplished with a variety of equipment, as determined by other factors such as terrain and tree size.

With roadside, landing, or central-yard processing, debris management must be addressed, although it does not substantially affect the selection between various equipment types.

# Weather and Climate

Adverse weather conditions can disrupt harvesting operations for any given day (e.g., it may be too rainy for skidders, too windy for fallers, or too foggy for helicopters to operate). Even though the exact days that will be affected cannot be predicted, planners usually account for some shutdowns to occur based on local climate, or long-term average weather patterns.

### OPERATIONAL

Weather mainly has an impact on operating techniques, rather than on equipment selection. Some ways that weather influences harvesting operations include:

- Heavy rainfall increases the risk of unacceptable soil disturbance by skidders because of high soil moisture content.

- High wind increases the safety hazard for fallers.

- Dense fog reduces visibility, making grapple yarding difficult.

- High wind and dense fog make flying helicopters unsafe.

- Hot, dry weather increases the chances of fires starting on cable-yarding cutblocks because of friction from rubbing cables. Other potential sources of ignition include high-speed saws on feller-bunchers and sparks from tracked machines working on rock.

- Cold weather makes branches more brittle, and easier for delimbers to remove.

- Dense snow caused by slight warming improves the traction for wheeled skidders.

- Deep snow covers the felled timber and makes footing unsafe for choker-setters on cable yarders.

Each machine type is influenced by weather in its own way. Wet weather typically affects ground-based equipment more than cable equipment. Yarders are more affected by wind and poor visibility than ground-based equipment. Helicopters are most influenced by poor weather since they require safe flying conditions. Occasional days lost to poor weather conditions are accepted as a cost of doing business, but the average frequency of shutdowns caused by weather must be considered.

**Figure 159**

*Operating ground-based equipment on sensitive soils during wet weather can result in site degradation.*

The long-term weather, or climate, will often influence the annual work schedule, especially as it relates to seasonal operating areas. In coastal areas, operations typically move from the high elevations in summer to low elevations in winter to make operations easier. Such problems as icy roads, slippery footing on steep sideslopes, and logs buried under the snow are minimized. In contrast, Interior operations usually favour winter conditions when frozen ground and snow cover reduce the risk of causing soil disturbance. Logs buried under the snow are less of a problem with ground-based systems because the delay between falling and skidding is usually less than for yarding. With less time between phases, the risk of unexpected snowfall is reduced.

Although equipment selection is driven primarily by terrain and timber, the climate may influence the choice in some situations. For example, when choosing between skyline or helicopter systems, a high number of foggy or windy days would favour the skyline over the helicopter. Also, climate and soil conditions may work in combination. For example, the summer operating season for skidders may be too short to be economical, while the longer operating season of forwarders may favour their use.

These influences of weather and climate pertain to operating techniques, rather than to the equipment selection itself. For the most part, equipment selection is guided by terrain and timber considerations, while the weather and climate simply affect the way that the equipment is used. Flexibility is the key to working with weather — have alternative areas to which to move the equipment if weather conditions force the closure of the current area.

### ENVIRONMENTAL

Wet weather increases soil moisture content, and the risk of causing unacceptable soil disturbance with ground-based systems. On steep sideslopes with cable systems, poor weather can increase the risk of slope failures. This effect is most pronounced along the standing timber edge, where high winds can cause windfall which can trigger slope failures. The slope failures may cause stream sedimentation. Environmental problems usually occur during bad weather.

However, bad weather affects the choice between equipment types less than the timing of operations. If the ground is too steep for environmentally safe ground-based equipment during wet weather, it is also likely to be too steep during dry weather.

## EXTERNAL REQUIREMENTS

External requirements are characteristics of the operating environment that can be changed by human interventions. They are not inherent characteristics of the site, and may change from time to time. The external requirements have been divided into three classes: forest management considerations, corporate policies and business practices, and layout and development.

### Forest Management Considerations

Harvesting operations on managed forest land are subject to plans and decisions made at higher levels, and harvesting activities must conform to the requirements of various legislation, permits, or management regimes. These requirements are usually outside the control of the planner or logging contractor to change.

#### Silvicultural system

A variety of silvicultural systems is used in British Columbia, including clearcutting, selection, shelterwood, and seed tree. One aspect of the planning process is to choose a harvesting system that is compatible with the silvicultural system.

Clearcutting is the predominant silvicultural system in British Columbia, and all of the har-

**Figure 160**
*A small tower yarding uphill from a partial cut in the Interior.*

vesting systems can clear-cut. Accordingly, the silvicultural system is not an issue when selecting the harvesting system if clearcutting is planned.

The other silvicultural systems can be broadly grouped as various forms of partial cutting. In choosing the harvesting system, the question is "What are the implications of using different harvesting systems under various partial cutting prescriptions?" There are two broad issues: (1) the equipment must be able to maneuver itself and the harvested logs in confined spaces without damaging the residual trees and site, and (2) often the equipment must be able to work economically with less harvested volume than is typical for clearcutting on similar sites.

Often, the same equipment used for clearcutting can be used for partial cutting, but with more operating constraints and at a reduced productivity rate. This method of operation may suffice for a few cutblocks, but for a steady program of partial cutting, equipment optimal for the task is desirable.

**Figure 161**
*A forwarder working in a partial retention system in the Interior.*

The machinery used for partial cutting must be able to travel safely within the confined spaces of a corridor cut through the standing timber. Forwarders are especially well suited to this task because the logs are cut short and carried, making them easy to maneuver between the standing trees without damaging the residual trees. Small skidders and tractors are also well suited to the task, but clambunk skidders are ill suited because of their size and limited maneuverability. Small skyline yarders, both single-span and multi-span, are suitable for partial cutting, but large skyline yarders are unsuitable because of their high cost.

The falling method must be matched to the subsequent yarding or skidding method. If the trees are hand-felled, the yarding or skidding equipment must be able to reach the felled trees from the travel corridor. Grapple-equipped machines, either skidders or yarders, are poorly adapted to partial cutting operations with hand-falling. Furthermore, highlead systems are unsuitable for partial cutting because they can reach only as far as the choker length will allow. Instead, skyline systems with slackpulling carriages work better.

Grapple machines can be used if the trees are bunched after falling. Bunching can be done with a feller-buncher, a feller-processor, or a loader-forwarder. In this context, a loader-forwarder would build bunches in the corridor for a yarder or skidder to move to the landing. An important feature to consider for falling or bunching machines is the superstructure design: "zero clearance" machines are designed with minimal superstructure overhang, making them suitable for working within narrow corridors without damaging the residual stand.

Feller-bunchers can reach only as far from the trail as their boom will allow, making it necessary to locate the corridors fairly close together. Loader-forwarders are similarly

**Figure 162**
*A loader-forwarder working in a partial cut, moving the trees from the felling site into a corridor for subsequent yarding with a swing yarder.*

limited, although they need only to reach to the felled trees rather than all the way to the stump. Some feller-processors have extendible booms to reach farther into the stand, making them able to work from more widely spaced trails.

Faller safety is a concern for partial cutting systems. Every tree could become hung up during falling, which creates a safety hazard. Worker safety is much improved with mechanical falling. In addition, feller-bunchers and feller-processors can better control the falling direction of the trees, which may reduce breakage of both the cut trees and the residual trees.

Proper layout, including payload analysis, is critical to achieving optimum productivity in partial cutting systems, especially because cutblock volumes are reduced compared with clearcutting. Layout and falling patterns that orient the trees in the direction of skidding minimize the amount of tree turning, which increases productivity and reduces damage to the residual stand. Keeping the trails as straight as possible is also beneficial.

Each phase of the operation must be coordinated to ensure that a timber supply is always available to minimize costs. Operating in several areas simultaneously may reduce costs.

Cable systems have the added requirement that suitable anchor and support trees must be found. Anchors and supports for subsequent entries into the stand using the same harvesting system should also be considered — several suitable supports should be left at each location to allow for tree mortality.

### ENVIRONMENTAL

The harvesting system for partial cutting must be capable of removing the logs without compromising the health of the forest. Therefore, breakage of standing trees (including advance regeneration), scarring, and soil degradation must be minimized. Falling trees, logs sweeping around corners, logs dragged to the inside of corners, machine travel, hits by the felling head, and whipping overhead cables are all potential sources for scarring and breakage. Multi-span skylines have the lowest potential of the cable systems for causing damage to residual trees because the cables are held within the corridor by the intermediate supports.

Residual trees can be protected by leaving rub trees in strategic locations. These trees, which absorb the damage instead of the residual trees, are removed during the final stages of harvesting. Another strategy is to protect the trees with barrels or other materials (Hedin 1994).

Scheduling the operations to avoid critical periods for tree growth can reduce the amount of scarring. Trees are most susceptible to scarring when the sap is running; that is, in the early spring and summer. Thin-barked species may also be more susceptible to scarring during very cold periods. The amount of soil compaction and damage to the trees' roots can be reduced by operating during dry, frozen, or snowpack conditions.

An additional consideration for selecting the falling equipment is to consider the ability to judge which trees to cut and which to leave. Visibility from the cab of a machine may be limited, although skylights can improve visibility. Several companies commented to FERIC during the interviews that hand-fallers can better judge which trees to cut and which trees to leave than an operator enclosed in a machine cab.

## Utilization standards

The choice of harvesting system may influence the utilization level, especially regarding breakage and stump height.

### OPERATIONAL

Mechanical falling can reduce the amount of breakage compared with hand-falling when the machine is matched correctly to the timber size. The falling direction can be controlled more precisely, which reduces the amount of breakage during falling, and the stems can be aligned for less breakage during skidding, yarding, or forwarding.

**Figure 163**
*Accumulating several trees before bunching improves efficiency in small timber.*

The choice of falling equipment is especially critical for small trees because of falling costs and volume recovery. Hand-falling becomes very expensive as the tree size decreases, and directional falling may be sacrificed in favour of speed. This action may result in more breakage during skidding; therefore, mechanical falling is usually preferred. Feller-bunchers with accumulator arms are ideal for cutting small trees, although there may be a tendency to simply knock over the smallest trees. If a feller-processor is substituted for the feller-buncher, the total volume recovered from the stand can be increased; since each tree must be cut individually with feller-processors, the additional cost to recover the volume instead of discarding the tree is low. However, productivity will still be low because of the small tree size.

Winter operations on a snowpack are typical for the Interior. Either hand-falling or mechanical falling is feasible in moderately deep snow, but too-deep snow will make it difficult for hand-fallers to cut stumps low enough to meet standards. Shovelling the snow away from the base of the tree may be required. In contrast, feller-bunchers can push down through snow to cut lower stumps. Feller-processors are less capable of cutting low stumps in deep snow because the saw head cannot be pushed through the snow very easily.

Fresh snowfall may conceal the trees after falling, and grapple-equipped skidders or yarders can dig through the snow to find the hidden logs.

Piling logs with a loader-forwarder in preparation for grapple yarding may make it easier to hook the logs and reduce breakage, especially for smaller trees. Piling the logs at a slight angle to the yarding direction may also make it easier for the operator to hook the logs.

The harvesting system may need some method for handling exceptional logs such as those too large for the mechanical falling equipment or special products such as poles and pilings. Hand-fallers working with choker-equipped machines are often more effective for these tasks than grapple-equipped machines. Large trees are often left until the surrounding small trees have been harvested, but different companies handle poles and pilings differently. They may be harvested either before or after the primary harvesting. Two-pass harvesting for special products is impractical with cable systems because of the high setup costs and the need for clearance for the cables.

ENVIRONMENTAL

Feller-bunchers with high-rotation heads are better able to buck windfalls than those with non-rotating heads. The wider range of rotation allows the head to be aligned with the stem without turning the feller-buncher itself. This can improve utilization and productivity, as well as reduce the soil disturbance caused by skidding the tracks.

**Figure 164**
*A feller-buncher head specialized for windfalls. The grapples can pick up fallen trees, or the head can be turned vertically for falling standing trees.*

### Soil disturbance guidelines

In recent years, minimizing the amount of soil disturbance has become a major consideration for harvesting operations. Various guidelines for different jurisdictions may set maximum allowable limits for soil disturbance based on parameters such as soil sensitivity ratings and soil disturbance hazards. In many cases, the requirement to manage the soil disturbance has changed the way that harvesting systems are selected and the equipment used.

Risk management, especially on marginal sites, lies at the core of these changes. On these marginal sites, the risk of causing unacceptable soil disturbance can be sufficient to choose different harvesting equipment than might have been selected in the past. Some immediate results of this risk-based approach are the deployment of cable systems instead of ground-based systems on steep or sensitive terrain, the introduction of tire-and-track systems such as forwarders and clambunks, the trend towards less summer logging in the Interior, and the more widespread use of helicopters. In most cases, these changes require more expensive equipment and methods and changes in operating techniques.

Although equipment selection may be founded on soil disturbance principles as defined in legislation, FERIC observed that equipment selection is generally considered in terms such as slope, terrain, soil conditions, and season, as described elsewhere in this handbook. The actual soil disturbance guidelines were not prominent in the selection process.

FERIC was also told many times during the interviews that operator attitude had a much greater impact on soil disturbance levels than the equipment itself. Properly trained and highly motivated operators are the best insurance for minimizing soil disturbance. Soil disturbance problems are often associated with a single-minded dedication to high production or poor planning.

Rehabilitation of disturbed areas can also be done after harvesting to restore soil productivity and prevent the effects of soil-degrading processes. However, these activities must be considered or planned prior to harvesting to ensure that rehabilitation measures are possible and appropriate for the site and soil conditions, and that any access structures such as skid trails are constructed in a manner conducive to successful restoration of soil productivity.

## Corporate Policies and Business Practices

Some characteristics of the operating environment are specified by corporate policies and practices, and are within the capability of the company to make changes.

### Operating season

In the British Columbia Interior, woodlands operations are typically associated with a specific mill, and the link between the two is often quite close. On the other hand, coastal woodlands and milling operations are usually separate, sometimes with little contact between them. However, in both cases, the mills typically operate year-round while the woodlands operations are more seasonal. Therefore, the woodlands operations must build a large enough log inventory to carry the milling operations through the shutdown period. Log inventories are expensive to maintain, and many managers attempt to reduce the costs by extending the operating season for as long as possible to achieve a more even-flow state.

Winter is the peak operating season in the Interior because ground-based equipment causes the least soil disturbance on snow or frozen ground. Operations are often shut down completely during spring breakup (when the frost is leaving the ground) and during fall freezeup (before the ground is frozen). Summer is a favourable operating period, but the number of cutblocks suitable for summer harvesting is often limited.

On the Coast, the typical seasonal constraints are winter shutdowns caused by snow and ice, and summertime curtailments caused by high fire hazard. Low-elevation winter operations are often scarce, and the peak operating times usually occur in the summer. The drier periods of spring and fall are also desirable operating periods.

Therefore, the key to extending the operating season in the Interior is to make more cutblocks available during the summer. On the Coast, the key is to make more cutblocks available during the winter.

Purchasing new equipment for extending the operating season is impractical unless the equipment can also be used economically for the remainder of the year. Furthermore, the benefit of extending the operating season must be weighed against any potential reductions in productivity or utility that may occur during the rest of the year. For example, forwarders can operate when skidders cannot, but they may be less productive and they require significant changes to the entire corporate wood flow.

#### OPERATIONAL

The seasonal limiting factor for woodlands operations depends on the geographic location. It is important to examine the complete operation to determine which phase is limiting and determine what can be done to extend the operating season.

For coastal locations, cable operations in deep snow are impractical because of the potential for overlooking logs buried under the snow. The long time period between falling and yarding increases the risk of losing logs underneath the snow. Furthermore, footing on deep snow on steep sideslopes and trucking on steep, icy hills are hazardous.

Aside from the seasonal limitations imposed by trucking, the key equipment factor for extending the operating season is to use grapple systems that do not require on-the-ground workers for setting chokers. Site factors to extend the operating season include moving to lower elevations where the snow depth is less, or to less-steep areas where the risk of logs sliding over the snow is reduced.

In most locations in the Interior, the limiting factor during early spring is the high trucking costs resulting from weight restrictions placed on public roads. In many cases, skidding and processing for roadside systems can continue as normal during the period of curtailed trucking. If the road is constructed to all-season standards, trucking can begin from the stockpiled logs before skidding begins. This practice is not feasible for landing-based systems because of the limited space for log storage.

ENVIRONMENTAL

Later in the spring, when trucking restrictions are lifted, is a critical time for many Interior operations because the log inventory at the mill is usually low, and there may be corporate pressure to begin harvesting. However, conditions in the cutblocks may not be optimal — operations on wet soils could cause excessive soil disturbance — so special techniques should be considered. Soft-footprint machines may be required. Feller-processors create a debris mat that can be used as a skid trail, and forwarders and clambunks with tracked-wheeled designs can travel where conventional skidders cannot travel. Cable systems may be able to begin operations before ground-based systems. Trucks with central tire inflation systems may be required to maintain the road surface.

## Timber flow

The purpose of a woodlands operations is to produce a flow of timber of the required species and grades at the appropriate times, but to accomplish this task, the harvesting equipment must work consistently. Every effort must be made to ensure that potential delays are identified and rectified before the scheduled starting date for operations. Many factors can cause delays: inclement weather, equipment failures, permit-approval problems, and the lack of roads into operating areas. A manager can control only some of these factors. Flexibility should be incorporated into the harvesting plan to account for delays beyond the manager's ability to control.

In addition to consistent timber flow being a requirement of the woodlands operation, it can also be a constraint on equipment selection. Consider that a delay in one cutblock can cause other delays, and possibly affect the availability of a specific piece of equipment. The optimal equipment may not be available when the cutblock is ready for harvesting, and an inferior machine or system may be substituted.

Another aspect of timber flow is producing the right species mix at the right time. Since different tree species grow on different sites, and the different sites may be better suited to different equipment, it follows that constraints on species mixtures will affect the equipment selection. For example, a typical situation for the Interior is for spruce-balsam stands to grow on the steeper ground, while the flatter ground supports pine stands. The spruce-balsam stands may be suited for winter logging with skidders because of the soil moisture, while the pine stands are available for summer logging. If the mills require spruce-balsam timber to be produced during the summer, a different harvesting system such as forwarders or cable systems may be required.

Such factors will affect each company's long-term equipment selection priorities, and equipment selection must be done individually according to corporate objectives.

## Mill specifications

Companies typically specify the sorts for species and grade to be delivered to the mills. The number of sorts depends on many factors, including the stand variability, the number of mills supplied from the operation, and the infeed configuration at the mills. The infeed configuration to the mill also influences whether long logs or cut-to-length logs can be

**Figure 165**

*Logs stored at roadside in a cut-to-length operation. Specialized trucks are required to transport these short logs, and the mill must also be properly configured.*

accepted. With long logs, the mill can maximize value, but this function is performed in the woods by the feller-processor in CTL systems. For CTL systems, the woodlands operations must work especially closely with the mill to ensure that the correct log specifications are being used.

In general, coastal operations commonly produce "camp run" truck loads and use a central location for sorting, while Interior operations sort in the woods. Six to eight sorts can be done in the woods, but a central sortyard is usually required with many sorts. A landing is required for six or eight sorts, but two or three sorts are feasible with roadside operations. Smaller landings make it more difficult to separate more sorts.

With roadside operations, all the logs are piled together, so the sorts must be identified by using slight variations of log placement within the pile. One technique — align the butts of one sort with the road edge, and the butts of the second or third sort offset by two or three metres — is sufficient for the loader to differentiate between the sorts.

### Amount of work available

The amount of work available directly influences the decision to purchase equipment. With an assured supply of suitable timber and terrain, companies or contractors can accept the financial risk required to purchase new equipment. Without a reasonable amount of work, they are reluctant to take the risk. Therefore, acquiring new equipment for a few cutblocks is not usually a viable option.

Another strategy is to use the same equipment in new ways. With this strategy, equipment that can be adapted to be used in different ways on different sites is desirable. Hydraulic excavators are an example of adaptable machines: excavators can be used as loader-forwarders, backspar machines, site-preparation scarifiers, and yarders. In contrast, forwarders are more specialized — their use is limited to transporting short logs or being a prime mover for site preparation equipment.

Some contractors specialize and move between regions to secure a full work schedule. Licensees also use the same technique internally (e.g., by alternating a helicopter crew between several divisions on a multi-year schedule). If travelling between sites, the amount of work at any location must be sufficient to amortize the mobilization costs at a reasonable rate. Another drawback for specialized contractors is that all licensees may want the equipment at the same time to comply with various environmental constraints. Everybody may need the equipment at one time, and then nobody may need it at another time. Such a business is difficult to operate.

Furthermore, cut controls limit the amount of timber that can be harvested each year, and any volume provided to a specialized contractor will likely be deducted from an existing contractor. The regulatory conditions of various tenures make it difficult to take volume away from existing contractors, so negotiations between company and contractor will be required.

## Unique methods

Canadian loggers will often devise new ways to log a difficult site using the available equipment, given the opportunity to try new techniques. During the interview process, FERIC saw several examples of this innovation.

Using two or more machines together in new ways was a prominent theme in the unique methods, especially using hydraulic excavators with other equipment. Loader-forwarding itself is a relatively new method, and has been used on various sites. The excavator's agility and flexibility are key to its widespread use with other machines. Out-of-lead or out-of-deflection

**Figure 166**
*This loader retrieved trees from within a riparian management zone, and bunched them away from the creek for a grapple skidder to skid them to roadside.*

pockets of timber can be loader-forwarded to within reach of a swing yarder. When fitted with a winch, the excavator can double as a yarder for sites where ground-based traffic is prohibited. One of the more innovative ideas mentioned during the interviews was to move excavators to the top of the hill to work with skylines. The skyline could help pull a large loader to the top of the hill, or a smaller loader could be flown to the top of the hill on the skyline.

Intermediate supports are not commonly used on skylines, although they can be used to solve some problems. Poor deflection is an obvious application for intermediate supports, but their use in partial cutting is increasing. Strips cut along the contours and harvested using skylines with intermediate supports were used on Vancouver Island to achieve visual screening from a well-used recreational lake.

Skidders have difficulty on adverse slopes, but not cable machines. On suitable sites, using a skidder at the bottom of a slope to forward timber to a highlead yarder can save a significant amount of road. In other circumstances, building one trail to the bottom of the hill may allow the skidders to skid the timber to the bottom of the hill without trails, and then follow the single trail back to the top.

Several methods were used for cut-to-length systems, all in an attempt to solve particular problems in particular circumstances. The classic method includes feller-processors and forwarders, but FERIC also saw feller-bunchers and processors working together to improve productivity.

The rationale for cut-to-length systems was questioned at one south-central Interior location that FERIC visited: the desired result was to leave more nutrients on-site, and the conven-

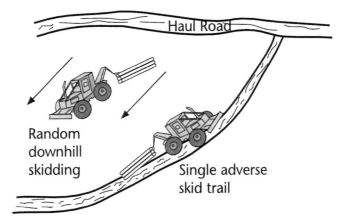
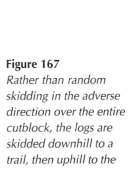

**Figure 167**
*Rather than random skidding in the adverse direction over the entire cutblock, the logs are skidded downhill to a trail, then uphill to the haul road. By eliminating the adverse random skidding, site disturbance can be reduced and productivity increased.*

tional thinking was to use feller-processors and forwarders in a cut-to-length system. The innovative solution was to use conventional equipment in a tree-length system, and to haul branches and tops back from the landing to the woods using the grapple skidder.

A consistent message heard during the interviews was that planners wanted to work within a permit-approval system in which the desired results after harvesting were stated, and let the loggers use their ingenuity to achieve those results.

### Labour availability and training

The most modern equipment will provide no better results than run-of-the-mill equipment if the operators are not properly trained in its use. This is especially true for environmental considerations such as soil disturbance — the importance of operator attitude and aptitude cannot be overstated. Many times during the interviews, FERIC was told that the operator was far more important to the success of a type of equipment than the equipment itself.

**Figure 168**
*Typical operating controls for a modern feller-processor. The operator must manage several hydraulic controls and monitor the computer system.*

New or specialized equipment often requires different skills than old equipment, and the operators must be given adequate time to adjust their operating techniques. Introducing new equipment to an operation does not guarantee that it will be used correctly or efficiently. Training is not limited to new equipment and techniques — maintaining a labour pool with traditional skills is also important. For example, techniques such as rigging backspars, intermediate supports, and skylines are not common knowledge in many highlead crews, and skilled hand-fallers may be scarce in some areas. Specialists may be required, but it is not always possible to obtain trained people on short notice or for a short duration. A specialized contractor may be the solution for a single project, but this method does not develop the required skill in the local labour pool.

Effective communications are vital for continued success. The operators must be made aware of the requirements and expectations for harvesting and the reasons for new prescriptions and techniques; they must also be trained in the skills necessary to achieve the desired results. Continued training is important. Workplace meetings between the operators, contractors, regulators, and licensees are vital to ensure that the correct message is communicated to the machine operators, and that their concerns and ideas are properly addressed. Including the resource agencies in the workplace meetings can help to ensure that the operators know exactly what is expected from an environmental perspective.

### Equipment availability and service

Nearly every piece of equipment eventually breaks down beyond the ability of local mechanics to repair, and the owner depends on the dealer's staff to return it to service. As their livelihood depends on quick repairs, loggers are generally reluctant to buy equipment unless supported by a nearby dealer; the security offered by a handy service depot is an important consideration in any purchasing decision. Some less-familiar brands of machinery do not have the extensive dealer network that the more familiar brands have developed, and the risk involved with choosing a less well-known brand must be factored into the purchasing decision.

The reputation of the machine regarding productivity and availability must also be considered. Canadian loggers and logging conditions are reputed to be hard on equipment, and robust designs are vital to achieve acceptable availability. Training programs offered by various dealers are also important, especially if they can instill proper equipment handling methods to reduce the incidence of breakdowns.

Local conditions play an important role in availability; for example, the trees may be larger in one region than another, which cause more wear and tear on the machine.

## Equipment transportation

The smaller cutblocks that result from the implementation of the Forest Practices Code make the cost of moving equipment more important than previously. The cost of moving the equipment is a fixed cost that must be amortized over the cutblock volume, and can become significant with small cutblocks. Reducing the moving time between cutblocks is important to reducing harvesting costs.

**Figure 169**
*Moving a large swing yarder via low-bed.*

Tracked equipment is slow to move, and generally requires a low-bed for moves of more than one or two kilometres. Wheeled equipment is more mobile, and can move between cutblocks more easily. Depending on the type, wheeled equipment can travel from a few to tens of kilometres without requiring a low-bed.

Large, tracked coastal equipment such as line loaders and yarders are almost always moved on low-beds, even for short-distance moves.

The overall machine size is a consideration when transportation on public highways is required. Some machines, especially large yarders, are so large that they must be dismantled to be moved, which significantly increases the moving costs. A large volume is required to amortize the moving costs at a reasonable rate. It is becoming more common for yarders to be designed for highway-legal transport without being dismantled. These machines, which have been common in the United States for some time, are newer to the British Columbia market.

For very large yarders, transportation even on private logging roads can be a problem, especially for areas with difficult road access. Bridges and culverts must be designed to accommodate the equipment load and be in good condition. Switchbacks and tight corners that can accommodate log trucks may still be too tight for large skyline towers or swing yarders with their booms lowered. The tower size, and its ability to handle tight corners, must be considered during road layout.

## Layout and Development

### Road location

Earlier in the forest industry's development in British Columbia, rail, flume, water, and animal transportation systems were used to move logs from the cutblock to the mill, but these methods have largely disappeared. Today, trucking predominates and a properly located, constructed, and maintained road network is required for efficient and environmentally sound operations.

A road network for timber harvesting usually consists of main roads, branch roads, and on-block spur roads. The design, location, and construction of main and branch roads are much less influenced by harvesting system considerations than with on-block spur roads. Other considerations such as total volume to be harvested, public access, and high-speed travel play a more predominant role.

Proper road location is a broad subject — the discussion here will focus on the linkage between road location and equipment selection. These two factors have a circular relationship: potential road locations are influenced by the proposed harvesting system, but if the road has already been constructed, the choice of harvesting systems is restricted by the road location. The normal engineering practice is to choose the harvesting system first, and then find a suitable road location. If a suitable road location cannot be found, then a different harvesting system with different road requirements must be considered. For example, skyline systems can reach farther from the road than highlead systems, and may eliminate the need for some road. Helicopters can significantly reduce road requirements.

#### OPERATIONAL

The road location must be accessible by the primary transport equipment, and be suitable to the log trucks. Thus, the road must be within skidding, yarding, or flying distance of each tree in the cutblock and in a location appropriate for the primary transport equipment. The road location must also meet the standards for grades, alignment, width, and strength appropriate to the log-truck fleet. Lastly, it must also meet environmental standards.

The road location should be considered for more than the immediate cutblock because choices made in one location can influence the options available in another location.

Ground and cable systems have different requirements for road location within the cutblock. In ground-based systems, the road should be located near the lowest elevation in the cutblock to minimize the amount of adverse skidding. In contrast, uphill yarding is favoured for many cable systems, so a higher location within the cutblock is preferred. In locations with suitable terrain, ridgetop roads maximize the amount of uphill yarding; however, this requires an existing road on the top of the hill. More commonly, the cutblock is split, yarding a portion uphill and a portion downhill.

The critical point for deflection depends on the position of the yarder on the hill. For downhill yarding, deflection can be increased by moving the yarder farther from the hill. For uphill yarding, the critical point is often immediately adjacent to the landing because the yarder must be positioned away from the edge of the road to allow adequate space for landing the logs.

Whether the harvesting system is landing-based or roadside affects the usage and standard for the road. For landing-based systems, the road location between landings is less

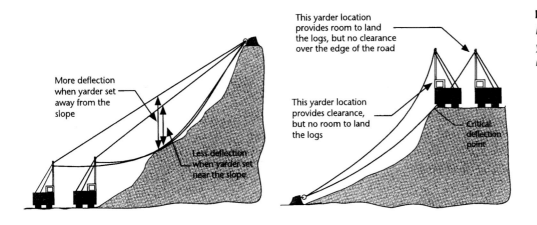

More deflection when yarder set away from the slope

Less deflection when yarder set near the slope

This yarder location provides room to land the logs, but no clearance over the edge of the road

This yarder location provides clearance, but no room to land the logs

Critical deflection point

**Figure 170**
*Deflection depends on yarder placement with respect to the slope.*

important than the landings themselves, and the road location is governed by the limitations of the log trucks. Maximum adverse and favourable grades are typical design constraints.

In contrast, the road itself must meet the requirements of the harvesting equipment in roadside systems. The adjacent area must be suitable for storing and processing logs, which means the sideslope cannot be too steep, and the loader has room to operate. In the Interior, roadside logging usually entails a butt 'n top loader operating on the space adjacent to the road, while on the Coast, a line loader operating from the road surface is typical. The limitation for swing loaders becomes the ability to stockpile the trees adjacent to the road. For butt 'n top loaders, a sideslope of 15–20% is the maximum, but line or hydraulic loaders can stockpile logs up to about 60% sideslope. The maximum road grade can also become a limiting factor; swing yarders can work safely up to about 12%, while line loaders are difficult to operate safely above 15%.

Two other factors also pertain to road location and ground-based roadside logging. First, the skidders must be able to drop the logs at the roadside and carry on travelling, which means there cannot be a high cut bank to travel over. Second, the ground adjacent to the road must be free of large obstacles so that the loader can travel. If these conditions cannot be met, then roadside logging may be unsuitable.

Cable systems are limited by deflection, so the road location must consider the ground profile across the entire cutblock. With swing yarders, this normally means checking deflection in parallel lines all along the road, but for highlead systems, deflection is checked in a fan shape from just the landing locations.

Locating the roads for cable systems in broken ground is a challenge because of limited deflection. Every part of the cutblock must be accessible to the road with adequate deflection and clearance — a rule of thumb is that the top half of the tower must be visible from every point in the cutblock. The amount of road required may be prohibitive, and multi-span skylines may be warranted to access some areas. Ground-based systems might be considered because they are not limited by deflection. Combining ground- and cable-based systems may make the timber accessible without additional road (e.g., by loader-forwarding to a grapple yarder from behind a ridge or over a deflection break).

### ENVIRONMENTAL

The largest source of sedimentation and slope failures is from truck roads, and, other things being equal, reducing the amount of road will reduce the risks associated with roads. Long-distance systems such as clambunks, skylines, or helicopters can reduce the amount of road. However, these systems are typically more expensive to operate than skidders or grapple yarders, and usually involve an economic tradeoff between amount of road and harvesting costs.

By locating roads to take advantage of variations in terrain to maximize the deflection, soil disturbance caused by yarding can be minimized.

Many additional environmental factors must be considered regarding road locations. Items such as road standards, stream crossings, ditch and culvert design, and cutbank height are critical, but do not pertain to equipment selection and are beyond the scope of this handbook.

### Landing location

Landings are the centre of activity for many systems, and their locations should be chosen carefully. The area must be large enough to accommodate the equipment for skidding or yarding, processing, sorting, and loading, plus room for decking logs, and their placement must be correct within the cutblock.

As with road location, this section discusses only the implications of landing location with respect to alternative harvesting systems and equipment. Many other factors can make one landing location preferable to another, but do not pertain to the difference between systems and are not discussed here.

#### OPERATIONAL

Landings, the centre of activity for many systems, are one of the most hazardous locations for workers, especially for cable yarding systems. Providing proper training for workers can help them to avoid accidents, but providing ample working space is equally important. Enlarging landings is easy on flat ground (within prescribed limits), but steep terrain makes it difficult to build large landings. To facilitate landing construction on steep terrain, landings can be built on a knoll or bench, excavated into the sidehill, built as two smaller, adjoining landings at different elevations ("stepped" landing), or built on a terrace. Not every site has a bench in a convenient location, so excavation is often required. Excavation is expensive, results in a high face that may be difficult and dangerous to yard over, and generates material that must be disposed of properly. Stepped landings require less excavation than single-level landings, and are a good way to reduce the amount of excavated material and the height of the excavated face. Terracing, or using cribwork to support a fill, is rare but may be warranted in unique circumstances.

An additional consideration on steep ground is the vertical angle of the guylines. The safe angle is prescribed by safety rules, and must fall within certain minimum and maximum angles. Achieving a low enough angle on the low side of the road, and a high enough angle on the high side of the road may prove difficult.

Alternatives to building large landings on steep terrain should be explored. Long-distance harvesting systems such as large skylines and helicopters allow the landing to be located away from the actual logging site on more favourable terrain. Swing yarders do not require landings because the timber can be piled on the road. A skidder can be used to forward the timber to a more favourable location for a landing.

In ground-based systems, the landing is usually located to optimize skidding. Downhill skidding is preferred, and the average skidding distance is minimized with the landing located near the centre of the cutblock. Other factors, such as the trees' orientation on the landing to enhance mechanical processing and loading, may also be considered for landing location.

The final landing location should be established during layout, well before road construction and falling begin.

**ENVIRONMENTAL**

The amount of excavated material and its placement should be considered when locating landings on steep cutblocks. The amount of excavated material can be minimized by locating landings on benches, and sidecast material is more easily contained. Locating a landing near a stream increases the risk of siltation. End-haul to remove excess material to another location may be required.

For cable landings, the requirement for guylines outside the perimeter of the landing should be considered. If a cable landing is located too near the edge of the cutblock, the guylines may infringe on plantations or standing timber. Anchors may need to be buried if the stumps are old, thereby requiring excavation in the plantation.

Again, alternative harvesting systems with different landing requirements should be considered if the environmental risk with the landing is too high.

## SELECTED BIBLIOGRAPHY AND SUGGESTED READING LIST

Andersson, B. 1994. Cut-to-length and tree-length harvesting systems in Central Alberta: a comparison. FERIC, Vancouver, B.C. TR-108. 32 p.

Andersson, B. and W. Jukes. 1995. Harvesting coastal second-growth forests: two case studies. FERIC, Vancouver, B.C. TN-232. 14 p.

Andersson, B. and F. Warren. 1996. Harvesting coastal second-growth forests: hand falling and skyline yarding. FERIC, Vancouver, B.C. TN-239. 14 p.

Andersson, B. and G. Young. 1997. Harvesting coastal second-growth forests: harvesting system performance and cost estimates. FERIC, Vancouver, B.C. TR-120. 50 p.

Araki, D. 1994a. Winter grapple yarding in the interior of British Columbia. FERIC, Vancouver, B.C. TN-211. 8 p.

———. 1994b. At-the-stump and roadside log processing in Alberta: a comparison. FERIC, Vancouver, B.C. SR-96. 29 p.

———. 1996. Increasing value and fibre recovery from coastal forests by manufacturing longer logs. FERIC, Vancouver, B.C. TN-247. 14 p.

Bennett, D.M. 1993. Partial cutting in a second-growth Douglas-fir stand in coastal British Columbia: productivity, costs, and soil impacts. FERIC, Vancouver, B.C. TN-199. 12 p.

———. 1996. Harvesting sensitive sites with a long-distance cableways system: productivity and costs. FERIC, Vancouver, B.C. TN-238. 13 p.

———. 1997. Partial cutting in mountainous old-growth forests in coastal British Columbia: harvesting productivity and cost, and residual stand impacts. FERIC, Vancouver, B.C. TR-119. 20 p.

Breadon, R.E. 1983. Timber development planning for the British Columbia Interior: the total-chance concept. FERIC, Vancouver, B.C. HB-4. 73 p.

British Columbia Institute of Technology. 1995. Introduction to forest harvesting. Vancouver, B.C. RRET 2442. 184 p.

Conway, S. 1976. Logging practices, principles of timber harvesting systems. Miller Freeman Publications, Inc. San Francisco, Calif. 416 p.

Favreau, J. 1997. A comparison of fiber loss during full-tree and cut-to-length harvesting. FERIC, Pointe Claire, Que. TR-118. 12 p.

Forrester, P.D. 1993. Observations of two Skylead C40 cable yarders. FERIC, Vancouver, B.C. TN-201. 8 p.

———. 1995. Evaluation of three cable-yarding systems working in a coastal old-growth forest. FERIC, Vancouver, B.C. TR-112. 17 p.

Gingras, J.F. 1988. The feller-buncher/grapple skidder system: optimizing bunch size. FERIC, Pointe Claire, Que. TR-081. 10 p.

————. 1990. Harvesting methods favouring the protection of advance regeneration: Quebec experience. FERIC, Pointe Claire, Que. TN-144. 8 p.

Gingras, J.F., D. Cormier, J.C. Ruel, and D. Pin. 1991. Comparative study of the impact of three skidding methods on advance regeneration. FERIC, Pointe Claire, Que. TN-163. 12 p.

Gingras, J.F. and A. Godin. 1997. Sorting for quality with a cut-to-length system. FERIC, Pointe Claire, Que. TN-255. 6 p.

Hedin, I.B. 1994. Shelterwood harvesting in coastal second-growth Douglas-fir. FERIC, Vancouver, B.C. TN-216. 10 p.

————. 1996. Shelterwood harvesting with a skyline system in a coastal second-growth forest. FERIC, Vancouver, B.C. TN-243. 8 p.

Hunt, J.A. 1995. Commercial thinning a coastal second-growth forest with a Timberjack cut-to-length system. FERIC, Vancouver, B.C. TN-235. 14 p.

Kockx, G.P. and D.L. De Long. 1994. Return-trail skidding: pilot study. FERIC, Vancouver, B.C. TN-218. 10 p.

Kockx, G.P. and R.K. Krag. 1993. Trials of ground-skidding methods on steep slopes in the east Kootenays, British Columbia: productivities and site impacts. FERIC, Vancouver, B.C. SR-89. 23 p.

Larson, R.S. 1978. Compendium of major cable logging systems. Interforest AB, Stockholm, Sweden. 112 p.

Lyons, C.K. 1997. Analysis of line tensions and backspar stresses in a skyline system: a pilot study. FERIC, Vancouver, B.C. TN-258. 8 p.

MacDonald, A.J. 1989. A review of mechanical delimbers in Western Canada. FERIC, Vancouver, B.C. TR-093. 27 p.

Makkonen, I. 1988. Review of forwarders. FERIC, Pointe Claire, Que. TN-123. 12 p.

————. 1989. Choosing a wheeled shortwood forwarder. FERIC, Pointe Claire, Que. TN-136. 12 p.

Meek, P. 1996. Effects of skidder traffic on two types of forest soils. FERIC, Pointe Claire, Que. TR-117. 12 p.

Meek, P. and J.A. Plamondon. 1996. Effectiveness of cut-to-length harvesting at protecting advance regeneration. FERIC, Pointe Claire, Que. TN-242. 12 p.

Mitchell, J.L. 1996. Trial of alternative silvicultural systems in southern British Columbia: summary of harvesting operations. FERIC, Vancouver, B.C. TN-240. 11 p.

Novak, W.P. 1988. Downsizing skidders with high-flotation tires. FERIC, Pointe Claire, Que. TN-113. 6 p.

Phillips, E.J. 1996. Comparing silviculture systems in a coastal montane forest: productivity and cost of harvesting operations. FERIC, Vancouver, B.C. SR-109. 42 p.

Plamondon, J.A. and J. Favreau. 1994. Establishing the optimal skidding or forwarding distance as a function of road cost. FERIC, Pointe Claire, Que. TN-219. 8 p.

Richardson, R. 1988. An introduction to off-road processors and harvesters. FERIC, Pointe Claire, Que. TN-126. 12 p.

Studier, D.D. 1993. Carriages for skylines. Oreg. State Univ., For. Res. Lab., Corvallis, Oreg. 14 p.

Studier, D.D. and V.W. Binkley. 1974. Cable logging systems. U.S. Dep. Agric. For. Serv., Portland, Oreg.

Workers' Compensation Board of British Columbia. 1981. Yarding and loading handbook. Vancouver, B.C. 188 p.

———. 1991. Fallers' and buckers' handbook. Vancouver, B.C. 132 p.

———. 1992. Grapple yarder and super snorkel handbook. Vancouver, B.C. 176 p.

———. 1993. Cable yarding systems handbook. Vancouver, B.C. 172 p.

Young, G.G. 1997. Mechanical and manual bucking of coastal second-growth stands: a comparison of value recovery. FERIC, Vancouver, B.C. TN-267. 12 p.

# INTERVIEW SITES

The following table lists the sites where FERIC visited or telephoned during the interviews for the handbook. The comments summarize FERIC's impression of the operation — they should not be interpreted as complete descriptions of the operations. Instead, these comments highlight the features that FERIC felt distinguished the division.

Interviews were conducted via telephone (T) or on-site (O/S). The on-site interviews often included a field trip to view the operations in person.

| Company | Location | Interview Type | Comment |
|---|---|---|---|
| **Industrial** | | | |
| Ainsworth Lumber Co. Ltd. | 100 Mile House | O/S | Primarily feller-buncher and skidder systems working to roadside or landings. Decking at roadside with a loader improves skidder productivity. Small component of cable yarding. |
| Ainsworth Lumber Co. Ltd. | Lillooet | O/S | Primarily cable systems on steep ground on transition between coastal and interior conditions. Small skylines used in partial cutting prescriptions. Ground-based systems confined mainly to winter operations except for one cut-to-length operation. Minor component of helicopter and loader-forwarding. |
| Ainsworth Lumber Co. Ltd. | Savona | O/S | Using buncher, processor, and forwarder in a cut-to-length operation. |
| Babine Forest Products Ltd. | Burns Lake | T | Mainly roadside logging with conventional skidders. Substantial portion is processed at the stump. Also use small cable yarder, helicopter, and cut-to-length with forwarder. |
| Bell Pole Co. Ltd. | Salmon Arm | O/S | Skyline yarding with a small tower equipped with motorized carriage. Various partial cutting prescriptions to address the visual-quality objectives. |
| Bell Pole Co. Ltd. | Terrace | T | Primarily ground-based equipment operating from landings. |
| Canadian Forest Products Ltd. | Woss | O/S | Variety of equipment ranging from loader-forwarders to super snorkels to swing yarders and large skylines. Operate primarily on private land. |
| Crestbrook Forest Industries Ltd. | Cranbrook | O/S | Wide range of site conditions including substantial amount of steep ground results in large amount of cable yarding. Typically using small skyline towers with motorized carriages and intermediate supports. Ground-based skidding often uses return-trail layout. Hand-falling and bunching with loaders in some |

| Company | Location | Interview Type | Comment |
|---------|----------|----------------|---------|
| | | | areas. Using feller-processor and forwarder in cut-to-length operations where terrain and stand conditions are suitable. |
| Federated Co-op Ltd. | Canoe | T | Primarily skidders in landing and roadside configurations. About 20% is cable logging with swing yarder and small skylines. |
| Gorman Brothers | Westbank | T | Mixture of grapple skidders, forwarder, and highlead tower. Primarily roadside processing. |
| Houston Forest Products Co. | Houston | O/S | Conventional, ground-based equipment, primarily used in roadside operations. Cutblocks with large tree sizes are designed for landing operations to accommodate hand-bucking. Large range of tree size requires range of equipment sizes. |
| International Forest Products Limited | Campbell River | T | Typical coastal highlead and swing yarders. |
| International Forest Products Limited | Hope | T | Highlead tower and swing yarder. Helicopter logging on alternate years to help reduce mobilization costs. |
| International Forest Products Limited | Squamish | O/S | Conventional coastal logging with towers and grapple yarders. Some helicopter logging. |
| International Forest Products Limited | Tofino | T | Swing yarders and highlead towers, with a minor amount of loader-forwarding. Helicopter logging on alternate years to help reduce mobilization costs. |
| JS Jones Timber Ltd. | Boston Bar | O/S | Transition between Interior and Coast. Have reduced ground-based systems from 30 to 5% of harvesting because of steep ground. Now primarily use large highlead towers. |
| JS Jones Timber Ltd. | Pitt Lake | T | Grapple yarder and highlead towers. |
| Lignum Ltd. | Williams Lake | O/S | Cut-to-length system in the western part of the operating areas allows for increased volume recovery from small trees. Using tree-length system to roadside or landings where the tree size is larger. Cannot switch completely to cut-to-length system because the mill must retain tree-length capability to accommodate wood purchased from independent sources. |
| MacMillan Bloedel Ltd. | Eve River | T | Mixture of swing yarders, large skyline, and highlead yarders. Considering a Wyssen skyline in specific situations. |

| Company | Location | Interview Type | Comment |
|---------|----------|----------------|---------|
| MacMillan Bloedel Ltd. | Kelsey Bay | O/S | Variety of equipment ranging from loader-forwarders to swing yarders to large skylines. |
| MacMillan Bloedel Ltd. | Menzies Bay | O/S | Primarily loader-forwarders, super-snorkel, and swing yarder. Using highlead towers as required. |
| MacMillan Bloedel Ltd. | Powell River | T | Primarily swing yarders, although one large skyline is also used. Mechanized operations in second growth, using feller-processor and loader-forwarders. Occasional use of grapple skidders. |
| MacMillan Bloedel Ltd. | Shawnigan | O/S | Second-growth harvesting using a combination of conventional and mechanized equipment. Dryland sort includes a chipping plant. Operating primarily on private land. |
| Northwood Pulp and Timber Ltd. | Houston | T | Primarily conventional skidders, either skidding to landings or roadside. Small amount of cable yarding with small towers, and a minor amount of helicopter. |
| Northwood Pulp and Timber Ltd. | Prince George | O/S | Two distinct operating conditions (pine flats and steep, wetter areas) are suitable for summer and winter respectively with conventional, ground-based equipment. Also use highlead and swing yarders year-round in the steeper areas with larger timber. |
| Pacific Forest Products Ltd. | Cowichan | O/S | Combination of conventional equipment (swing yarders and skylines) and cut-to-length system (feller-processor and forwarder). About 10% by helicopter. All operations on private land. |
| Pacific Forest Products Ltd. | Zeballos | T | Typical coastal mixture of loader-forwarders and swing yarders. One large skyline is new to the operation. |
| Pacific Inland Resources Ltd. | Smithers | O/S | Transition zone between coastal and Interior conditions requires range of equipment. Wide range of tree size influences equipment selection. Cable and ground-based systems both important. Using clambunk skidders on steep ground, especially for the longer skidding distances. Require low ground pressure equipment to extend the summer operating season. |
| Pope and Talbot Ltd. | Castlegar | O/S | Substantial amount of cable yarding including highlead, swing yarders, and skylines. Mechanical bunching after falling increases the productivity of yarders. |

| Company | Location | Interview Type | Comment |
|---|---|---|---|
| Pope and Talbot Ltd. | Midway | O/S | Proportion of non-clearcut has increased substantially, requiring contractors to alter their equipment fleets and operating techniques to adapt to small openings. Forest floor displacement hazard is a major concern in typical cutblocks. |
| Pope and Talbot Ltd. | Nakusp | T | About half the volume is from cable systems: swing yarders and small skylines. Remainder is mechanically felled and skidded with tracked or rubber-tired skidders. Some helicopter logging, and a very minor component of horse logging and loader-forwarding. |
| Repap B.C. Inc | Smithers | T | Variety of conditions in transition zone between Coastal and Interior requires a variety of equipment. Cable equipment is primarily small highlead. Ground-based equipment includes clambunk skidder. |
| Riverside Forest Products Ltd. | Armstrong | T | Mainly grapple and line skidders, with about 80% operating from landings and 20% from roadside. Small amounts of cable and helicopter logging. |
| Riverside Forest Products Ltd. | Kelowna | O/S | Variety of equipment and systems used on different sites. Cut-to-length system using feller-processor and forwarder in partial cuts. Full-tree harvesting to centralized sortyard. Specialized contractor for all right-of-way timber. Extensively using temporary roads to reduce skidding distance. |
| Skeena Sawmills | Terrace | O/S | Mainly cable equipment except for one rubber-tired skidder used sporadically, and a large component of helicopter logging. Very little loader-forwarding because of limited opportunity. |
| Slocan Group (was Timberwest at time of interview) | Mackenzie | O/S | Complete conversion to cut-to-length system to address several concerns including the inability to log during the summer with conventional equipment. Various models including single-grip and double-grip feller-processors. Unique self-propelled barge used for lake-borne transport. |
| Slocan Group | Radium | O/S | Over half of the cut is based on a "basal area cut" silviculture prescription that requires very careful operations to protect the understorey. Hand-falling is often required. Combination of ground-based and cable equipment, including a long-distance Wyssen skyline. All skidding is on designated trails because of high soil-compaction hazard. |

| Company | Location | Interview Type | Comment |
|---|---|---|---|
| Slocan Group | Vanderhoof | O/S | Almost entirely roadside operations with conventional, ground-based equipment. Using dangle-head processors because of the small tree size. |
| Timberwest Forest Ltd. | Campbell River | O/S | Highly mechanized operations in second-growth timber. Extensive use of feller-bunchers and dangle-head processors. Operating primarily on private land. |
| Timberwest Forest Ltd. | Crofton | O/S | Second-growth harvesting near urban areas using small tractors. Also use loader-forwarders, long-line skylines, and helicopters. All operations on private land. |
| Timberwest Forest Ltd. | Gordon River | O/S | Typical mixture of swing yarders, loader-forwarders, and highlead. Innovative use of large and small skylines. Using small, dangle-head processor in second-growth timber. Small tractor operates in selective cutting in second growth. |
| Timberwest Forest Ltd. | Sandspit | T | Swing yarders and large skyline. Using loader-forwarders on suitable terrain. |
| Tolko Industries Ltd. | Louis Creek | O/S | Steep-slope harvesting using tracked or flex-track skidders. Wide range of timber sizes requires wide range of equipment. |
| Tolko Industries Ltd. | Merritt | O/S | Range of site conditions requires a range of capabilities. Primarily using skidders from landings, but also have component of cable logging using small highlead tower. |
| Weldwood of Canada Ltd. | 100 Mile House | T | Primarily roadside logging with conventional skidders. Also use feller-processor and forwarder in a cut-to-length operation, as well as small tower and skyline. |
| Weldwood of Canada Ltd. | Quesnel | O/S | Combination of cable and ground-based equipment, including clambunk skidders. All operations are to the roadside. Using horses for selective logging in wildlife habitat areas. |
| Weldwood of Canada Ltd. | Williams Lake | T | Mainly skidders operating out of landings, with a smaller component in roadside configuration. Small amount of cable yarding. |
| West Fraser Mills Ltd. | Quesnel | O/S | Using tree-length to roadside system exclusively, including one with a grapple yarder. Two contractors use clambunk skidders to allow for more summertime operations. |

| Company | Location | Interview Type | Comment |
|---|---|---|---|
| West Fraser Mills Ltd. | Williams Lake | T | Conventional ground-based operations with about 25% as cable operations. Also have significant amount of volume harvested from selection cuts using conventional equipment. |
| Western Forest Products Ltd. | Holberg | T | Exclusively loader-forwarders, super snorkels, and swing yarders. |
| Western Forest Products Ltd. | Jordan River | T | Typical mixture of loader-forwarder, super snorkels, and swing yarders. |
| Western Forest Products Ltd. | Port McNeill | O/S | Extensive use of loader-forwarders and super snorkels, with cable systems relegated to "cleanup" functions. "Hands-on" style of supervision. |
| Weyerhaeuser Canada Ltd. | Kamloops | O/S | Conventional landing-based operations. Large portion of area in community watersheds, which affects road density and cutblock size. |
| Weyerhaeuser Canada Ltd. | Lumby | T | Combination of skidders operating from landings or from roadside, and small highlead tower. |
| Weyerhaeuser Canada Ltd. | Okanagan Falls | O/S | Primarily landing-based operations, with a component of roadside. One cable contractor with self-propelled carriage. Gradually changing from beetle-salvage to green-tree harvesting. Off-highway haul. |
| Zeidler Forest Industries | McBride | O/S | Combination of ground-based and cable systems, with the ground-based operations confined almost exclusively to winter. |

**Government**

| Company | Location | Interview Type | Comment |
|---|---|---|---|
| BC Ministry of Forests | Campbell River | O/S | Small Business Forest Enterprise Program uses a variety of equipment, ranging from ground-based to cable to aerial. Risk-based analysis is used to specify the harvesting system for each site. |
| BC Ministry of Forests | Chilliwack | T | Many recent sales have been for skyline or helicopter systems. |
| BC Ministry of Forests | Clearwater | T | Rubber-tired skidders, flex-track skidders, and horse logging. Significant portion harvested with small highlead towers and skylines. |
| BC Ministry of Forests | Cranbrook | T | Mainly tractors with hand falling. Minor amount of horse logging. |
| BC Ministry of Forests | Duncan | T | Very little activity in the Small Business Forest Enterprise Program. Previously used some skidders, but now exclusively loader-forwarders and small cable yarders. |

| Ministry | Location | Interview Type | Comment |
|----------|----------|----------------|---------|
| BC Ministry of Forests | Hazelton | T | Primarily skidders operating from landings. Some horse logging, and minor amounts of cable and helicopter operations. |
| BC Ministry of Forests | Houston | T | Primarily rubber-tired skidders in either landing or roadside configurations. Minor amount of horse logging, cable systems, and cut-to-length with forwarder. |
| BC Ministry of Forests | Kamloops | T | Primarily grapple skidders and small tractors. Minor amounts of helicopter, cable, and horse logging. Significant amount of selective cutting. |
| BC Ministry of Forests | Penticton | T | Small contractors with rubber-tired, tracked, or flex-track skidders. Lots of single tree selection. |
| BC Ministry of Forests | Port Alberni | T | Typical coastal mixture of highlead and swing yarder. Substantial portion of helicopter systems, and some loader-forwarding and horse logging. |
| BC Ministry of Forests | Port McNeill | T | Typical coastal highlead and grapple yarding. Minor amounts of loader-forwarding and helicopter operations. |
| BC Ministry of Forests | Prince Rupert | T | Typical coastal highlead and grapple-yarding equipment. Small component of hand-logging, A-frame, and helicopter. |
| BC Ministry of Forests | Revelstoke | T | Mainly highlead yarders and small tractor skidders. Minor amount of helicopter and skyline. |

# INDEX*

## A

adverse    *See* skidding
aerial    *See* helicopter
anchor **138**
 backspar 71, 138, 140, 153, 178
 guyline **72**, 79, 83, 183
 mobile backspar 82, 161
 tailhold **72**, 83, 138

## B

backspar    *See* anchor
backspar trail 82
balloon 86
bucker    *See* hand-bucking
buncher    *See* feller-buncher
butt 'n top    *See* loader

## C

cable    *See* yarding
capital    *See* cost
carriage 70, **75**, 81, **85**, 137, 152, 156, 170
chain flail    *See* processor
chains    *See* tractive system
cherry picker    *See* loader
chipper    *See* processor
choker **66**, **81**
 skidding 131
 yarding 124, 138, 152, 167
clambunk **55**, 147
 costs 10
 partial cutting 170
 roadside 127
 slope limit 151
 soil disturbance 66, 131, 173, 181
 terrain 156, 163
clearance    *See* deflection
compaction    *See* soil disturbance
cost 9, **10**, 162
 aerial 88
 falling 98, 110, 172
 processing 114, 117, 121
 skidding 50, 56, 58, 63, 64, 68, 128, 150
 yarding 75, 83, 137, 170
cutblock size **164**, 179
 falling 91
 helicopter 76
 loading 126, 149
 skidding 56, 121
 yarding 72, 83

cut-to-length    *See* system, cut-to-length
cycle time 51, 55, 63, 68

## D

dangle-head    *See* processor, dangle-head
daytime    *See* hours of operation
debarker    *See* processor
debris
 chipping 117
 falling 100, 150, 156
 forwarders 57, 131, 149
 helicopters 142
 loader-forwarder 60
 nutrients 148
 processing 93, 109, 115, 129, 148, 164
 yarding 71, 72, 81, 136, 138
defect    *See* timber characteristic
deflection 75, 82, 135, 152, 177, 181
 skylines 137, 139, 156
delimber    *See* processor
diameter measurement 120
downhill    *See* skidding or yarding
dropline    *See* carriage

## E

excavator
 adaptable 176
 feller-buncher 100, 106
 loader-forwarder    *See* forwarder
 mobile backspar 72, 138
 site rehabilitation 129
 trail construction 132

## F

feller-buncher 99, **102**
 falling direction 143, 144
 grapple yarding 150
 partial cutting 67, 133, 165, 170
 riparian zones 154
 skidding 56, 67, 82, 163, 177
 tree size 83, 162, 172
 utilization 172
feller-director 96, **104**, 162
 falling direction 143
feller-processor 96, 111, 115
 debris 175, 178
 falling direction 143, 170
 tree size 162
 utilization 150, 163, 166
flex-track    *See* tractive system

---

* Bold numbers reference key concepts of an index entry.

Queen's Printer for British Columbia©
Victoria

7610008475

To purchase additional copies order online at: **www.crownpub.bc.ca**
For additional information contact us at:
**Crown Publications, Queen's Printer**
**Toll Free:** 1 800 663-6105
**Email:** crownpub@gov.bc.ca

**CROWN PUBLICATIONS**
Queen's Printer | www.crownpub.bc.ca